Third Edition

ASNT
LEVEL II
STUDY GUIDE

Ultrasonic Testing
Method

The American Society for
Nondestructive Testing, Inc.

The second edition of this Study Guide was prepared by William Spaulding and George C. Wheeler.

Third edition
  first printing 7/16
  ebook 7/16

Errata, if available for this printing, may be obtained from ASNT's web site, https://asnt.org/errata.

ISBN: 978-1-57117-367-6 (print)
ISBN: 978-1-57117-368-3 (ebook)

Printed in the United States of America

Published by:
The American Society for Nondestructive Testing, Inc.
1711 Arlingate Lane
Columbus, OH 43228-0518
www.asnt.org

Edited by: Cynthia M. Leeman, Educational Materials Supervisor
Assisted by: Bob Conklin, Educational Materials Editor
Synthia Jester, Layout
Joy Grimm, Production Manager

Tim Jones, Senior Manager of Publications

ASNT Mission Statement:
ASNT exists to create a safer world by advancing scientific, engineering, and technical knowledge in the field of nondestructive testing.

Cover photo credit:
Tessonics Corp.

FOREWORD

Purpose

This Study Guide is intended to aid individuals preparing to take the ASNT NDT Level II examination for ultrasonic testing (UT).

The material in this Study Guide addresses the body of knowledge included in *ANSI/ASNT CP-105: ASNT Standard Topical Outlines for Qualification of Nondestructive Testing Personnel.*

The ASNT NDT Level II certification program is a service offered by The American Society for Nondestructive Testing, Inc., that gives NDT personnel an opportunity to have their familiarity with the principles and practices of NDT assessed by an independent body. The program uses an independent body to review credentials and uses comprehensive written examinations to identify those who meet the criteria for becoming an ASNT NDT Level II.

How to Use the Study Guide

This Study Guide is designed to assist in the preparation for the ASNT NDT Level II examination. It is not intended to be the only source of preparation. The Study Guide provides a general overview of subject matter covered by the examination so that students can identify those areas of the body of knowledge in which they need further study.

Read through the text of the Study Guide, and if the discussion covers unfamiliar material, the references should also be studied. The review questions at the end of each chapter should be answered. Success in answering the questions will help determine if more concentrated study in particular areas is needed. Those familiar with some of the topics may wish to go directly to the review questions. If the questions can be answered confidently and correctly, additional study may be optional.

Additional Information

This Study Guide contains additional methods and/or techniques not required for ASNT UT Level II exam preparation.

In the 2011 editions of *SNT-TC-1A* and *CP-105*, phased array and time of flight diffraction were added as Level II techniques under UT.

Chapters on phased array (PA) and time of flight diffraction (TOFD) were added to provide basic information on these two techniques.

Chapter 5 — Time of Flight Diffraction was written by David Mandina, and Chapter 6 — Phased Array was written by the late Michael Moles. These chapters do not cover the topic completely, but are intended as a starting point for additional study. ASNT does not offer a certification examination on TOFD or PA at this time.

Standalone study materials on TOFD and PA may be published by ASNT in the future.

All chapter review questions are now multiple choice with four unique answers to more closely match the ASNT exam format.

Because ASNT is an International System of Units (SI) publisher, throughout the text both SI and imperial units are used. For simplicity, many equations in this book use 25 mm equals 1 in. Where SI units are not used in the original text of the standards and codes, conversions to SI units were not made.

This third edition Study Guide builds on the second edition written by William Spaulding and George C. Wheeler.

ACKNOWLEDGMENTS

The American Society for Nondestructive Testing, Inc. is grateful for the volunteer contributions, technical expertise, knowledge, and dedication of the following individuals who have helped make this work possible.

Technical Reviewers

David Alleyne – Guided Ultrasonics Ltd.
John A. Brunk
James R. Cahill – GE Measurement & Control
Eugene V. Charpia – Bluegrove NDT Consulting
John Chen – Schlumberger
Guillaume Courtemanche – Tenaris
Claude D. Davis – TUV Rheinland Industrial Solutions, Inc.
James B. Elder III – Savannah River National Laboratory
Philip E. Fish – Fish & Associates, Inc.
Nirav Dave – Ratnamani Metals & Tubes, Ltd.
Aaron DePoala – General Dynamics Electric Boat
Steven C. Johnson, Jr. – OneSubsea
Danny L. Keck
Thomas E. McConomy – ATI
Michael McGloin – NDT Enterprises
Scott D. Miller
Sepand Momeni – Mistras Group, Inc.
Luis A. Payano – Port Authority of NY & NJ
Michael J. Ruddy – NOV Tuboscope
John M. Sellers – Intertek Asset Integrity Management, Inc
Robert E. Stiger – Acuren Group, Inc.
Michael Sullivan – Olsson Associates
Kenneth White – Tenaris Hickman
William J. White – Forged Components, Inc.

Chapter Authors

David Mandina – Mandina's Inspection Services, Inc.
Michael Moles – Olympus NDT

Publications Review Committe

Joseph Mackin – Reel Group
Martin T. Anderson – Alaska Technical Training
Mark R. Pompe – West Penn Testing Group

REFERENCES

The following references were used to develop this Study Guide.

Workman, G.L. and D. Kishoni, technical eds., Patrick O. Moore, ed. *Nondestructive Testing Handbook*, third edition: Volume 7, *Ultrasonic Testing*. Columbus, OH: The American Society for Nondestructive Testing, Inc. 2007.

Marks, P. *Ultrasonic Testing Classroom Training Book*. Columbus, OH: The American Society for Nondestructive Testing, Inc. 2015.

ASNT Level III Study Guide: Ultrasonic Testing Method, second edition. Columbus, OH: The American Society for Nondestructive Testing, Inc. 2014.

Additional References

Krautkramer, J. and H. Krautkramer. *Ultrasonic Testing of Materials*, fourth edition. New York: Springer-Verlag, Inc. 1990.

McGonnagle, W.J. *Nondestructive Testing*, second edition. New York: Gordon & Breach, Science Publishers, Inc. 1975.

Metals Handbook: ninth edition, Volume 17, *Nondestructive Evaluation and Quality Control*. Materials Park, OH: ASM International. 1989.

Phased Array References

Ciorau, P., D. MacGillivray, T. Hazelton, L. Gilham, D. Craig, and J. Poguet. "In-situ Examination of ABB l-0 Blade Roots and Rotor Steeple of Low-Pressure Steam Turbine, Using Phased Array Technology," *15th World Conference on NDT*, Rome, Italy, October 2000.

Clay, A.C., S-C. Wooh, L. Azar, and J-Y. Wang. "Experimental Study of Phased Array Beam Characteristics," *Journal of NDE*, Vol. 18, 2 (June 1999): 59.

Davis, J.M. and M. Moles. "Back to Basics: Beam Sweeping vs. Encoded Data Collection," *Materials Evaluation*, Vol 65, 6 (2007): 539-541.

Dubé, N. "Electric Resistance Welding Inspection," *15th World Conference on NDT*, Rome, Italy, October 2000.

Ginzel, E.A. and D. Stewart. "Photo-Elastic Visualisation of Phased Array Ultrasonic Pulses in Solids," *16th World Conference on Nondestructive Testing*, Montreal, Canada, August 2004.

Lafontaine, G. and F. Cancre. "Potential of Ultrasonic Phased Arrays for Faster, Better and Cheaper Inspections," *NDT.net*, Vol. 5, 10 (2000).

Lareau J.P and R.M. Plis. "Phased Array Imaging First Use Qualification Effort: BWR Feedwater Nozzle Inner Radius Inspection from Vessel OD for a US Nuclear Power Plant," *NDT.net*, Vol. 7, 5 (2002).

Whittle A.C. "Phased Arrays – Panacea or Gimmick?" *Insight-Non-Destructive Testing and Condition Monitoring*, 46, 11 (2004): 674-676.

Wüstenberg, H., A. Erhard, and G. Shenk. "Some Characteristic Parameters of Ultrasonic Phased Array Probes and Equipments," *NDT.net*, Vol 4, 4 (1999).

CONTENTS

CHAPTER 1
Overview

History of Ultrasonic Testing

Ultrasonic testing (UT) is a nondestructive testing method that uses high-frequency (>20 000 Hz) sound waves to inspect materials for surface and subsurface discontinuities.

Scientists had investigated continuous wave techniques which used high-frequency acoustic waves for nondestructive testing in the 1930s. The early inspection techniques relied on the transmission of ultrasound through the part from a transmitting unit to a receiving unit, which limited inspection to parts that could be accessed on opposite sides. The level of sensitivity obtainable with these early methods allowed the detection of only those discontinuities that obstructed the ultrasound transmission and, in effect, were relatively large.

These early limitations were overcome in the 1940s by the use of pulsed ultrasonic waves. Pulse-echo inspection techniques were developed where ultrasound is both transmitted and received from the same side of the part. Pulse-echo ultrasonic testing is capable of detecting small discontinuities, determining their locations and depth, and estimating their sizes. This nondestructive testing technique has continued to develop into a sophisticated, reliable, and efficient inspection tool that is sometimes integrated with imaging software, and used in a variety of industrial applications.

Advantages and Limitations of Ultrasonic Testing

Ultrasonic testing is a versatile volumetric examination that is capable of usefully examining a wide range of thicknesses in many materials. For example, steel forgings up to 6 ft (2 m) in diameter and 18 ft to 20 ft (6 m to 7 m) long are regularly tested both radially and axially, as are much smaller sections such as thin-wall tubing or sheet metal 0.04 in. to 0.08 in. (1 mm to 2 mm) thick. For most ultrasonic testing applications, only one side of the object needs to be accessible and for many applications,

small, portable units are available. Ultrasonic testing is not hazardous to personnel, so the only safety precautions necessary are those practiced with any electrical equipment. A particularly useful feature of the method is its ability to measure quite accurately the depth of discontinuities from the test surface.

A limitation of the method is that it is not always reliable for detection of surface and near surface discontinuities. Very small parts, and those with irregular shapes or rough surfaces, small radii, large grain size, or inhomogenieties may be difficult or impossible to test. Precise lateral (side-to-side) location and accurate sizing of discontinuities is often not possible. Identification of the type of discontinuity found is usually very subjective, requires extensive experience, and is frequently debatable. Other methods such as electromagnetic testing, radiographic testing, liquid penetrant testing, or magnetic particle testing are often used in conjunction with ultrasonic testing to overcome these limitations.

Principles of Ultrasonic Testing

This section describes the basic elements of ultrasonic testing including the basic properties of acoustic waves and an overview of wave modes and search units.

Generation and Characteristics of Ultrasound

Ultrasound is usually generated by using electro-mechanical transducers called *piezoelectric materials*. These materials deform when subjected to an electric potential or voltage. If the potential alternates from positive to negative, the piezoelectric material expands when subjected to one polarity and contracts when the polarity is reversed. Therefore, alternating electrical current, usually in the form of a unidirectional spiked or square pulse is used to excite the piezoelectric material to convert the electrical energy to mechanical vibrations. The opposite effect also applies, that is, mechanical vibrations imposed on a piezoelectric material cause the material to generate alternating electric voltages. Therefore, a transducer may act as both a generator and a detector of ultrasonic waves.

Acoustic Waves

When a molecule is displaced from its position of equilibrium within a material, it exerts a force on adjoining molecules and transmits its motion or energy to them before returning to its steady state position. In this manner, acoustic waves (including ultrasound) are transmitted away from the original source. The transmission of acoustic waves is similar to the action that occurs when a stone is dropped into water and the ripples spread out in all directions. Although the wave (and its associated energy) travels away from the source point, there is no net transport of water. The wave peaks and troughs correspond to maximum upward and downward displacements of the water molecules from the steady water level.

The simplest ultrasound wave is a continuous wave in which the molecules are continuously displaced back-and-forth in a repetitive way. Each repetition of the molecule displacement is 1 cycle. The frequency of the continuous wave ultrasound wave is the number of cycles a molecule goes through in a unit of time and is measured in cycles per second (cps), or hertz (1 Hz is equal to 1 cps).

Velocity, Wavelength, and Frequency

Velocity is the distance traveled by the ultrasound in a unit of time, and it is measured in meters per second (m/s) or inches per second (in./s). Wavelength is the distance between two molecules that are experiencing the same displacement in consecutive cycles, as shown in Figure 1.

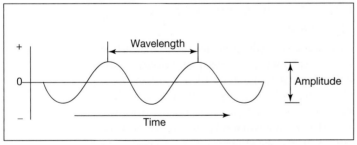

Figure 1: Sound wave.

The mathematical relationship of these characteristics is defined in Equation 1.

$$\text{(Eq. 1)} \quad \lambda = \frac{V}{f}$$

where
   V is velocity,
   f is frequency,
   λ is wavelength.

The velocity of ultrasonic waves depends on the density and the elastic constants of the material in which the waves propagate. It is usually independent of frequency except for some special cases, such as lamb waves.

As illustrated in Equation 1, any change in frequency results in a corresponding change in wavelength — as the frequency increases, the wavelength decreases, and conversely, as frequency decreases, wavelength increases.

Like ordinary, audible sound waves, ultrasonic waves can bend around obstacles that are small compared to the wavelength of the ultrasound. Therefore, frequency selection is of prime importance because even under favorable conditions, discontinuities must have at least one dimension (perpendicular to the beam) that is greater than or equal to $\lambda/2$ in order to be detected. The best frequency to use for a specific inspection is a compromise between the smaller discontinuity size that can be detected with smaller wavelengths and the greater depth of penetration obtained with lower frequencies. Frequencies that are commonly used for inspecting various product forms are listed in Table 1.

Table 1: Test frequency for various forms.

Product Form	Test Frequency
Castings	200 kHz–5 MHz
Forged/rolled materials (sheet, plate, bar, and forgings)	1–5 MHz
Drawn/extruded materials (pipe, tube, bar, and rod)	2–10 MHz
Welds	1–5 MHz
Composites/ceramics	20 kHz–5 MHz

Amplitude and Energy

The amplitude of the ultrasound wave is the maximum displacement of the molecules from their position of equilibrium. The energy of the ultrasound wave is proportional to the square of the amplitude. Relative changes in ultrasound energy are measured in decibels, which is a logarithmic scale. An increase of 6 dB in the acoustic energy will double the signal amplitude on the display, a 100% increase — while a 40 dB increase will raise the amplitude 100 times.

Types of Waves (Modes)

Ultrasound can propagate in different vibrational modes, which differ in the direction(s) of particle displacement relative to the direction of wave propagation. Longitudinal (compressional), shear (transverse), surface (rayleigh), and plate (lamb) waves are frequently used ultrasonic wave modes.

Longitudinal Waves

Longitudinal waves — also called *L-waves, compressional-waves,* or *p-waves* — have a molecular (particle) motion or displacement that is parallel to the direction of wave propagation (Figure 2). A snapshot of the material would show regions of lower and higher density alternating in the propagation direction as molecules pull and push the molecule in front of them. This wave is similar to the wave obtained with a long coil spring when one end is moved sharply back-and-forth along the axis of the spring. These waves are the easiest to generate and detect, and are the only type that can be propagated not just in solids, but also in liquids and gases. In most ultrasonic testing applications, the ultrasound energy originates as longitudinal waves, which are converted to other modes that can be used for the particular test application.

Shear Waves

Shear waves (transverse waves or S-waves) have a molecule displacement that is perpendicular to the direction of propagation. (Both horizontal and vertical shear waves [SH and SV] are recognized, but they are beyond the scope of this book.) When molecules in a plane perpendicular to the wave propagation move sideways, this sliding motion is transferred to the next plane of molecules through a shear force (Figure 3). This wave penetrates appreciable distances only in solids — it may penetrate a short distance in highly viscous liquids. Shear wave velocity is approximately half of the velocity for a longitudinal wave in the same material. As a result, shear waves have about half the wavelength, twice the sensitivity of longitudinal waves having the same frequency.

Surface Waves

Surface (rayleigh) waves have an elliptical wave motion and propagate along the surface of the test material. They are generally considered to have a depth of penetration into the material of approximately one wavelength. Therefore, they are useful

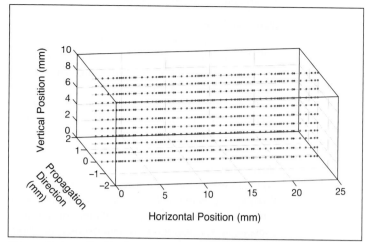
Figure 2: Longitudinal wave propagation and particle motion.

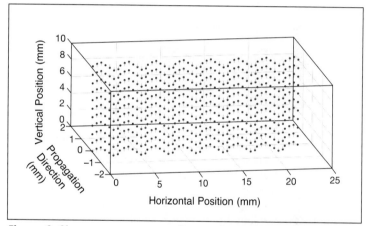
Figure 3: Shear wave propagation and particle motion.

for detecting surface and near-surface discontinuities, but not for deeper discontinuities. Surface waves are very sensitive to surface discontinuities, surface contaminants (for example, grease, paint, or scale), and uneven distribution of the couplant.

Lamb Waves

Lamb waves (plate waves) can propagate in plate-like objects if the frequency, material thickness, and beam entry angle are properly related to each other. They differ from surface waves and shear waves in that the entire part vibrates as the wave propagates parallel to the surface. Unlike surface waves, they are not readily absorbed by couplants. However, they are not widely used because there is no regular relationship between discontinuity size and response — each application requires development.

Propagation of Ultrasound

Beam Spread
Because of a fundamental physical phenomenon called *diffraction*, the ultrasonic beam gradually spreads out as it propagates, becoming broader as it gets farther from the transducer. Because no energy is added as the beam propagates, the spread decreases the intensity of the beam. The farther the beam travels, the less intense it becomes.

Near Field/Far Field
For a simple, nonfocused search unit, as the beam travels away from the search unit, it develops zones that have different characteristics. One, close to the transducer, is called the *near field* (*fresnel zone*) and the other, away from the transducer, is the *far field* (*fraunhofer zone*) (Figure 4).

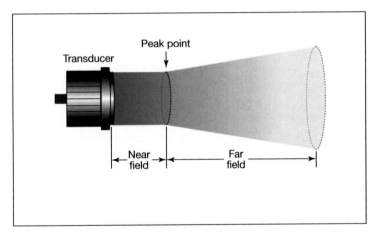

Figure 4: Zones within the ultrasonic beam.

In the near field, phase reinforcement and cancellation causes the beam energy to vary irregularly with location within the beam. As a result, in this region, the amplitude of an indication from a reflector is not related to the size of the reflector. While often unavoidable, the near field region is not preferred for inspection.

When the wavelength is small relative to the transducer diameter, the length of the near field increases with the transducer diameter and frequency, according to Equation 2:

$$\text{(Eq. 2)} \quad N_0 = \frac{D^2}{4\lambda}$$

where
N_0 is the near field length,
D is the diameter of the transducer,
λ is the wavelength of the ultrasound.

In the far field, the beam spreads at a constant angle (in a cone shape, for circular transducers) and the ultrasound energy decreases in a monotonic manner with distance from the search unit. Therefore, the amplitude of an echo from a reflector in the far field is related to the reflector size. For this reason, it is desirable to perform the inspection in the far field of the search unit whenever possible.

It is useful to know the beam width at any point in order to determine what region of the test object is being scanned. In the far field, this can be calculated from the transducer diameter and the ultrasound frequency. In general, the beam spread half angle decreases with the search unit diameter, or frequency increasing, approximately according to Equation 3.

$$\text{(Eq. 3)} \quad \sin \gamma = \frac{1.22\lambda}{D}$$

where
γ is half beam angle in degrees,
λ is wavelength of the ultrasound,
D is diameter of the transducer.

Attenuation
The reduction in energy of an ultrasound wave as it propagates through material is called *attenuation*, which is a material-related parameter. In addition to beam spreading, scattering and absorption of the sound are the major factors responsible for attenuation.

Scattering is related to the wavelength of the ultrasound and to the size and anisotropy of the metallurgical grains in the test object. Anisotropy is the condition of having different properties in different crystallographic directions within the grains. These differences in properties result in refraction, diffraction, or reflection of small amounts of the sound as it traverses grain boundaries and adjoining grains. Scattering is usually negligible when the wavelength is at least 100 times the average grain diameter, but if it is less than 10 times the grain diameter, useful testing of many materials may be problematical due to high levels of *noise* or *grass*.

Absorption is caused by friction between molecules of the test material. Scattering increases with the frequency of the ultrasonic wave.

Reflection
Sound continues to travel through a medium until it reaches a boundary of that medium. At a boundary, the propagation of the sound is reflected,

refracted, transmitted, or some combination of these effects. Which effects occur is dependent upon the acoustic impedances of the materials on both sides of the boundary and the angle at which the waves strike the boundary.

Acoustic impedance, Equation 4, is defined as the product of density of the material and the velocity of the ultrasonic wave.

(Eq. 4) $Z = \rho V$

where

 Z is impedance,
 ρ is density,
 V is velocity.

If the incident sound wave travels perpendicular to the boundary and the boundary surface is smooth, part of the sound wave energy is reflected and part is transmitted. In terms of energy, the amount of sound that is reflected depends on the impedances of the materials at the boundary, as shown in Equation 5.

(Eq. 5) $R = \dfrac{\left(Z_2 - Z_1\right)^2}{\left(Z_2 + Z_1\right)^2}$

where

 R is reflection coefficient,
 Z_1 is acoustic impedance of material 1,
 Z_2 is acoustic impedance of material 2.

Note, in terms of energy, R is never less than 0.

If the boundary is rough, rather than smooth, some of the sound will be scattered or diffracted, which changes the amplitude of the reflected beam.

Refraction

If the incident sound wave strikes an interface at an angle of incidence other than normal, the transmitted portion of the sound wave may be refracted. As shown in Figure 5, the transmitted energy takes a direction different from that of the incident beam. The degree of refraction that occurs is determined by the angle of incidence and the sound velocities in the materials at the boundary.

The angular relationship between the propagation direction of the incident and refracted acoustic waves depends on the respective acoustic velocities of the materials. This is expressed by Snell's law as stated in Equation 6, where the angles are measured

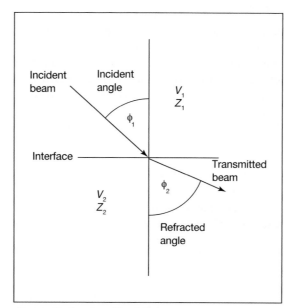

Figure 5: Angle of incidence.

between the direction of propagation and a line that is perpendicular to the test surface.

(Eq. 6) $\dfrac{\sin \phi_1}{\sin \phi_2} = \dfrac{V_1}{V_2}$

For example, a longitudinal wave in water ($V_1 = 1.49 \times 10^3$ m/s) striking a steel boundary ($V_2 = 5.85 \times 10^3$ m/s) at a 5° angle of incidence (ϕ_1) is transmitted in the steel at a refracted angle, ϕ_2, of 20°.

Critical Angles

In angle beam testing, as the angle of incidence is increased the first critical angle is reached when the refracted longitudinal beam angle reaches 90°. At this point, only shear waves exist in the second medium. As the incident angle is increased further, the second critical angle is reached when the refracted shear beam angle also reaches 90° and only surface waves are produced.

Mode Conversion

Snell's law can also be applied for a mix of acoustic modes if the appropriate acoustic velocities are used. For instance, in the previous example, although the wave propagating in the first material is a longitudinal wave, part of the refracted energy will be converted to a shear wave. This is called *mode conversion*. Using the velocity of shear waves in steel (3.23×10^3 m/s) as V_2, a

Snell's law calculation shows that a shear wave propagates in the steel at an angle of 10.9° with respect to the surface perpendicular (Figure 6). This shear wave will be in addition to the refracted longitudinal wave (that is, both will be present).

Mode conversion can also occur in the case of reflected energy and Snell's law can be used to find the angle of the mode converted wave reflected from the interface. For example, if a longitudinal wave is incident from steel to water with an angle of 70°, two waves will be reflected in the steel — one will be a longitudinal wave also at 70° and the other will be a mode converted shear wave with an angle of 31.3° (Figure 7).

The angle of the refracted beam increases with respect to the incident beam when the second material has a greater acoustic velocity than the first material and decreases when the second material has a lower acoustic velocity. In the first case, if the incident angle is continuously increased, at a certain point the refracted angle will be 90°. For larger angles, the phenomenon of total internal reflection occurs, where no ultrasound penetrates the second material. The incident angle for this condition is called the *critical angle*. If the second material is a solid, two critical angles exist — a smaller angle for longitudinal waves (first critical angle) and a larger angle for shear waves (second critical angle).

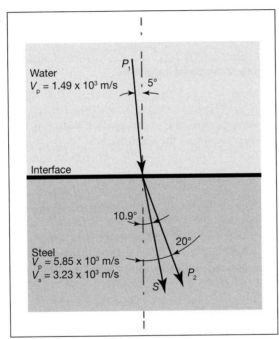

Figure 6: Longitudinal mode conversion from water to steel. P_1 is incident longitudinal wave, P_2 is refracted longitudinal wave, S is refracted shear wave.

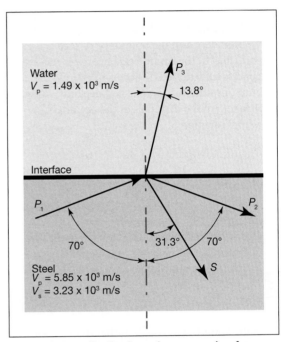

Figure 7: Longitudinal mode conversion from steel to water. P_1 is incident longitudinal wave, P_2 is reflected longitudinal wave, P_3 is refracted longitudinal wave, S is refracted shear wave.

Review Questions

1. Another name for rayleigh waves is:

    a. surface waves.
    b. longitudinal waves.
    c. shear waves.
    d. transverse waves.

2. A limitation of ultrasonic testing is:

    a. its low sensitivity to small discontinuities.
    b. its limited penetration power.
    c. it is not always reliable for detection of near surface discontinuities.
    d. the need for access to two surfaces of the object.

3. Snell's law is used to determine the relationship of:

    a. frequency and velocity.
    b. the angle of incidence and the angle of refraction.
    c. longitudinal velocity and contact angle.
    d. frequency and attenuation.

4. The depth that surface waves can penetrate a material:

    a. is half the material thickness.
    b. depends on acoustic attenuation.
    c. is one-tenth of the material thickness.
    d. is one wavelength.

5. Use the formula below to calculate the angle of refraction (ϕ_2) for a longitudinal wave passing through an interface of water-to-steel if the angle of incidence (ϕ_1) is 12°. Note: sound velocity is 1.49×10^5 cm/s in water (V_1) and 5.85×10^5 cm/s in steel (V_2).

    Snell's law:

    $$\frac{\sin \phi_1}{\sin \phi_2} = \frac{V_1}{V_2}$$

    a. 31.0°.
    b. 54.7°.
    c. 78.0°.
    d. 81.6°.

6. In angle beam testing, as the angle of incidence is increased the first critical angle is reached when the refracted longitudinal beam angle reaches:

    a. 10°.
    b. 32°.
    c. 45°.
    d. 90°.

7. Acoustic impedance is defined as the product of the density of the material and the:

    a. grain structure of the material.
    b. near field of the transducer.
    c. velocity of the ultrasonic wave.
    d. angle of the probe being used.

8. Shear wave velocity is approximately _____ the velocity for a longitudinal wave in the same material.

    a. one-half of
    b. one-tenth of
    c. twice
    d. three times

9. Plate waves differ from surface waves and shear waves in that:

    a. the sound wave diminishes as the wave propagates perpendicular to the surface.
    b. the entire part vibrates as the wave propagates parallel to the surface.
    c. they are absorbed by couplants as the wave propagates parallel to the surface.
    d. the sound waves strengthen as the wave propagates perpendicular to the surface.

10. Lamb wave testing requires _____ to correlate the discontinuity size and amplitude of ultrasonic response.

    a. additional transducers
    b. higher frequency probes
    c. further development and testing
    d. more couplant

Answers

1a	2c	3b	4d	5b	6d	7c	8a	9b	10c

CHAPTER 2
Equipment

Ultrasonic testing equipment includes transmitters/pulsers, receivers, time-base generators, power supplies, displays, probes, and special circuits.

Transmitters/Pulsers

A transmitter/pulser is an electronic signal generator that imposes a short interval of high-frequency alternating voltage on the transducer. The transmitter/pulser, along with the clock circuit, controls the repetition rate, pulse duration, and damping of ultrasonic signals.

Clock Circuits/Time-Base Generators

The clock circuit produces timed pulses, a reference voltage, and a reference waveform. The clock coordinates the operation of the entire electronic system.

Repetition Rate

A control available in many ultrasonic testing instruments is the repetition rate, which determines the number of times per second that a pulse is transmitted. Other instruments tie the repetition rate to the range control so that the repetition rate is preset for each choice of coarse range. Higher pulse repetition rates provide better discontinuity detection for high speed, automated scans. If the repetition rate is too high, a new pulse will be transmitted before the arrival of the echoes from prior pulses, resulting in ghost or *wraparound* signals. On cathode ray tube (CRT) displays, higher repetition rates provide a brighter display.

Pulse Duration

Pulse duration is the length of time the pulser imposes a voltage on the transducer, as determined by the clock circuit. The longer the pulse duration, the greater the transmitted energy and the larger the dead zone, which reduces near surface resolution. A longer pulse limits the precision in time measurements and gives reduced resolution. It would be difficult to discriminate between two reflectors that are closer together in depth (time) than the length of the pulse.

Receivers

The receiver (high-frequency pulse amplifier) electronically amplifies the signals returned from the test object to the receiving transducer and modifies these signals into a form suitable for display. The output from the receiver (after amplification) is a signal directly related to the intensity of the ultrasonic wave striking the receiving transducer. The bandwidth of the amplifier affects the resolution and sensitivity of the ultrasonic test, as will be discussed later.

Power Supplies

Power supply circuits provide the current for all functions of the ultrasonic instrument. These circuits are usually energized by conventional 115 V or 230 V alternating current in the case of stationary units. Portable ultrasonic instruments can also be powered by batteries.

Displays

Ultrasonic data is displayed in either video or radio frequency mode. In radio frequency, the cycles in each pulse are shown on the screen. In video mode, only a rectified envelope of the pulse is shown. Most ultrasonic testing instruments now use a digital flat panel display screen. However, older equipment uses analog video displays on a cathode ray tube, which is basically an oscilloscope. The horizontal deflection (sweep) voltages are synchronized by the clock circuit with pulses from the signal generator. The vertical deflection voltages are provided by the amplifier output signal.

Sweep/Gain Circuits (CRT Displays)

In an analog instrument, the sweep circuit is little more than a sawtooth voltage applied to a pair of horizontal deflection plates. When the voltage increases, the electron beam is driven across the screen. When the voltage drops, the beam starts again based on the clock signal.

Sweep or Zero Delay

The sweep or zero delay shifts the timeline without expanding or contracting it. The operator uses the sweep or zero delay to move the signal horizontally and to fix the origin to a desired time or depth. For example, during immersion testing, a long delay is generally used when starting the display at the test surface of the object because the signal from this surface arrives after a relatively long time of flight through the water.

Sweep Length or Range

The sweep length or range control determines the total time (depth) shown in the display. This control lets the operator fix the horizontal scale for the desired number of distance units per display division (for example, 5 mm/division).

Gain

The gain control determines the electronic amplification factor and, therefore, the displayed amplitude of the signal peaks. Gain control is generally calibrated in decibels. During standardization, the operator selects the gain so that the reference signals have the required amplitude.

A-Scan Displays

In an A-scan system, the amplitudes of the ultrasonic signals are displayed as a function of the time of flight through the material, as shown in Figure 1. Peak 1 is the transmission pulse, peak 2 could be a discontinuity, and peak 3 could be a reflection from the back wall. If the ultrasound propagates along a single homogenous material, and does not change acoustic modes, its velocity is constant. Therefore, the distance (time) between signals is proportional to the distance that separates the sources of the signals. The vertical height of the display is proportional to the amount of reflected ultrasonic wave commonly referred to as the amplitude of reflected sound.

B-Scan Displays

The B-scan data presentation is a cross-sectional view of the test object. One axis of the display shows the position of the search probe along the surface while the other axis shows the distance from the surface to the echo. The front and back surfaces of the object are profiled on the display. The position, orientation, and depth of a discontinuity along the cross section are displayed in profile as shown in Figure 2.

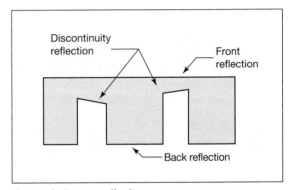

Figure 2: B-scan display.

C-Scan Displays

C-scan data presentation provides a plan view of the test object as shown in Figure 3. A gated area or *depth window* is selected so that only echoes arriving within the time frame corresponding to the depth of

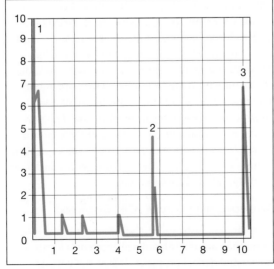

Figure 1: A-scan display: (1) front surface pulse signal; (2) discontinuity signal; (3) back reflection signal.

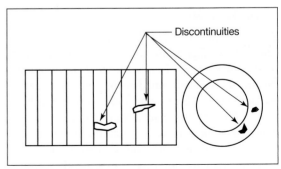

Figure 3: C-scan recording display.

interest are displayed. The display presents a projection of the shape of the discontinuities found within the depth window and the intensity or color of the display indicates the reflection strength. These displays may be printed on paper and kept as a permanent record. Many systems allow the signal to be gathered digitally, displayed on a computer screen, and stored on disk for later printing. These computerized imaging systems are used to process and enhance ultrasonic testing signals, which are presented in a color form for depth with a lookup scale that allows interpretation of the displayed data as shown in Figure 4. Quantitative analysis of the size, depth, or other characteristics of a discontinuity can be made using various options of the computer software.

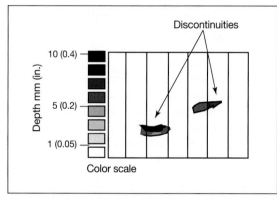

Figure 4: Color-display density scale.

Probes/Search Units

As discussed earlier, the generation and detection of ultrasonic waves involves the use of electro-mechanical transducers. Some common transducer materials used in ultrasonic probes or search units are listed in Table 1 together with their advantages and disadvantages. Most transducers today are based on some form of polarized ceramic such as lead zirconate titanate. Quartz, the primary material used in search units in the 1940s, is rarely used today because of its low efficiency.

Types of Probes

The most widely used types of probes are straight beam and angle beam contact probes, and flat and focused immersion probes. Various special application probes include dual element, delay line, and surface wave probes.

Contact Probes

Straight beam probes generate a sound wave, usually a longitudinal wave, in the test object at an angle perpendicular to the test surface.

Angle beam probes generate an ultrasonic beam in the test object at an angle less than perpendicular to the material surface. Angle beam probes usually consist of a longitudinal wave, straight beam probe with a wedge-shaped plastic contact shoe that causes the beam to strike the test surface at an angle. As discussed earlier, Snell's law of refraction at the wedge/part interface will then generate a mode-converted shear wave within the test object.

Because a refracted longitudinal wave may also be produced in the object, and having two beams present simultaneously would be confusing to interpret, most angle beam probes are designed so that the incident angle is between the first and second critical angle. This ensures that the longitudinal wave suffers total reflection and only the shear wave is transmitted in the object.

Because the refracted angles depend on the relative velocity of the shoe and the object material, and the velocity of the shoe or object material may not be known, it is good practice to standardize angle beam probes on the type of material they will be used to test.

Immersion Probes

Immersion probes (flat and focused) are straight beam, longitudinal wave units. However, they can also be used for angle beam inspection by angling the probe so that the beam strikes the test surface at the desired angle of incidence. The water takes the place of the angled contact shoe described above.

Because immersion probes are immersed in water, they must be thoroughly waterproofed and well grounded.

Some immersion probes are designed to focus the beam within the test object. There are at least two types of focused units. Spherically focused probes produce a point focus in the test object. They are usually used to test plate material. Cylindrically focused probes are also made. They produce a focused line in the test object, and are particularly used for testing pipe and tube. Focusing a beam is done by attaching a lens-shaped shoe to the flat face of the transducer. The purpose of focusing the beam is to concentrate the ultrasound within the test object at a certain distance from the test surface, thereby increasing the test sensitivity in that region. As can be seen by Snell's law, the focal length will change if the object material is changed. (Changing the water path length also has an effect, but it is usually minor.)

Probes for Special Applications

Special contact search units called dual element (dual transducer) probes can be used for thickness measurement of thin sections or for detecting discontinuities close to the test surface. These probes consist of separate transmitter and receiver elements housed in the same casing. The two elements are electrically and acoustically separated by the use of an acoustical barrier. The transducers may be mounted side-by-side for straight beam testing or stacked for angle beam testing. A pitch-catch technique has separate transmit and receive elements, such as a dual element transducer, through-transmission, and time of flight diffraction.

Other special contact search units designed for detecting discontinuities close to the material surface have an attached stand off (delay line), which amounts to a thick-soled shoe. The result is that the near field stays mostly inside the probe. The delay line also has the advantage of delaying the arrival of any echo from the test object to a time after the initial (transmit) electrical pulse has decayed, which further improves near surface resolution.

Rayleigh wave (surface wave) probes are built in the same way as angle beam search units, except that the incident angle is adjusted so that the incident angle is about 10° beyond the second critical angle. Therefore, no energy is transmitted to the bulk of the material and the incident wave is mode converted to a surface wave.

Probe Design

Case

A search unit case usually consists of a metal housing that contains the transducer, electrode, backing material, grounding wires, and a wear face that covers the transducer. The case provides stability and a coaxial electrical connector such as BNC, microdot, UHF, or LEMO for cable connection to the instrument.

Backing Material

Backing material provides damping of the transducer oscillations and mechanical support for the transducer. Damping is necessary to reduce the oscillations (ringing) of the transducer after the electrical/mechanical impulse ceases, in order to improve resolution. To do this, the backing material should have a high acoustic impedance to match

Table 1: Search unit materials and properties.

Material	Advantages	Disadvantages
Quartz	Electrical and thermal stability; insoluble in most liquids; mechanical stength; wear resistance; uniformity; resistance to aging	Low conversion efficiency; least efficient generator
Lithium sulfate	Easily dampened; intermediate conversion efficiency; negligible mode interaction; excellent receiver	Fragile; maximum temperature of 165 °F (74 °C); soluble in water
Lead zirconate titanate	High conversion efficiency; mechanical strength; moderate temperature range	High sensitivity cannot be fully exploited because of its high acoustic impedance
Barium titanate	Mechanical strength; good generator	Depolarizes with age; efficiency changes with temperature/mode conversion
Lead metaniobate	Low mechanical damping; high tolerance to temperature	High dielectric capacitance

the piezoelectric material, and be capable of absorbing the rearward-directed waves that are produced. Materials such as epoxy, rubber, plastics, or composites are commonly used for backing.

Electrodes

Electrodes are primarily silver or gold deposited on the piezoelectric element. The effects of variations in electrode thickness on the performance of transducers can be minimized by using the thinnest electrodes possible.

Transducers

For ultrasonic frequencies greater than 200 kHz, piezoelectric materials are generally used for transducers. Common materials include quartz, lithium sulfate, and polarized polycrystalline ceramics. As shown in Table 1, these materials vary considerably with regard to their efficiency in transmitting and receiving sound waves, their tolerance for high temperatures, and their stability in water.

Wear Face

A good wear face for contact straight beam probes combines ease of movement and wear resistance. Thin layers of aluminum oxide, sapphire, ruby, boron, or carbides are commonly used. Probes for immersion testing seldom include a wear face.

Resolution

Resolution is the ability of an ultrasonic testing inspection system to separate the ultrasound reflections from two discontinuities that are located close together in time, depth, or distance from the probe. To obtain high resolution, it is necessary to use a highly damped probe and a wide-band amplifier with flat phase curves in the vicinity of the probe frequency.

Sensitivity

Sensitivity is the ability of an ultrasonic testing inspection system to detect small discontinuities. As discussed earlier, to detect a discontinuity, the wavelength of the ultrasonic testing beam must be no more than twice the largest dimension of the discontinuity perpendicular to the beam. In addition, the signal produced by the discontinuity must be large enough to be noticeable on the display. Therefore, in general, sensitivity is increased by using higher frequencies and higher power pulses, and minimizing the beam spread, either by probe size or focusing.

Sensitivity is usually measured by the amplitude of response from artificial discontinuities in a reference block.

Special Circuits

Special circuits provide control of additional variables such as gates and distance amplitude correction/time controlled gain. Such circuits may or may not be provided on a particular instrument, but may often be purchased as options.

Gates

Gates are electronically controllable time periods that may be set up on the instrument display to correspond with specific zones within the test article. Signals appearing within the gated region may automatically operate visual or audible alarms. The gated signal may also be used to trigger a C-scan device for a permanent record. Gates have three basic controls — gate start, gate length, and gate threshold (alarm level or sensitivity). Gates can be set for positive or negative operation, that is, the gate will be triggered by a positive (rising) or negative (falling) signal within the gated region. For example, a positive gate could be used to trigger on a discontinuity indication, while a negative gate might be used to trigger on a reduction of the back reflection.

Distance Amplitude Correction/Time Controlled Gain

Distance amplitude correction and time controlled gain are electronic circuits that compensate for the difference in the amplitude of signals received from different depths in a test object. Such circuits allow the operator to avoid sketching a distance amplitude correction curve on the face of the display.

Review Questions

1. The type of display that never shows the entrance surface reflections is:

    a. an A-scan.
    b. a B-scan.
    c. a C-scan.
    d. an immersion scan.

2. Search units used in contact angle beam testing:

    a. can use a plastic wedge.
    b. generate longitudinal waves at an angle smaller than 90°.
    c. have a constant angle for different inspected materials.
    d. are always used in through-transmission mode.

3. A C-scan presentation depicts the:

    a. amplitude of the discontinuity.
    b. location of the discontinuity from the back surface.
    c. plan view of the discontinuity.
    d. depth of the discontinuity.

4. If the repetition rate is too high, a new pulse will be transmitted before the arrival of the echoes from prior pulses, resulting in:

    a. multiple signals.
    b. ghost signals.
    c. smaller signals.
    d. larger signals.

5. The longer the pulse duration, the greater the transmitted energy and the larger the dead zone, which reduces the ability to:

    a. transmit sound.
    b. detect small defects located near the back surface.
    c. detect defects located near the front surface.
    d. properly calibrate the instrument.

6. Immersion probes (flat and focused) are:

    a. straight beam, shear wave units.
    b. angle beam, longitudinal wave units.
    c. angle beam, shear wave units.
    d. straight beam, longitudinal wave units.

7. Rayleigh wave (surface wave) probes are built in the same way as angle beam search units, except that the incident angle is adjusted so that the mode converted shear wave in the test object is transmitted at about:

    a. 5% beyond the first critical angle.
    b. 10% beyond the second critical angle.
    c. 10% beyond the first critical angle.
    d. 5% beyond the second critical angle.

8. Damping is necessary to reduce the _____ of the transducer after the electrical/mechanical impulse ceases, in order to improve _____.

    a. noise, sensitivity
    b. oscillation, resolution
    c. oscillation, calibration
    d. noise, resolution

9. In general, sensitivity is increased by using higher frequencies and higher power pulses, and minimizing the beam spread, either by:

    a. velocity and diameter.
    b. crystal type or frequency.
    c. probe manufacturer or connector type.
    d. probe size or focusing.

10. Distance amplitude correction and time controlled gain are _____ that compensate for the difference in the amplitude of signals received from different depths in a test object.

    a. electronic circuits
    b. capacitors
    c. internal EMAT transducers
    d. resistors

Answers

1c   2a   3c   4b   5c   6d   7b   8b   9d   10a

CHAPTER 3
Techniques

Ultrasonic Testing Techniques

The most widely used ultrasonic testing techniques are the straight beam and angle beam pulse-echo techniques. Other techniques for discontinuity detection include pitch-catch (separate transmit and receive elements) and through transmission. Table 1 lists some typical product applications. Resonance testing is usually confined to thickness measurement and bond testing. Special processes may be used to overcome particular problems, such as testing of coarse-grained materials and for measurement of crack depth.

Couplant

Regardless of the technique used, it is usually necessary to use a couplant material between the transducer and the test object, because air is a relatively poor transmitter of sound waves. There is a great impedance mismatch between air and most materials to be tested. As a result, very little of the sound generated by the transducer is able to enter the test object through a layer of air, even if that layer is very thin. Use of a couplant reduces the impedance mismatch by eliminating air and substituting a material with an impedance nearer to that of the test object. Most couplants are liquids such as water or oils, or semiliquids such as gels or greases. In some cases, it is possible to use soft, rubberlike, solid materials as couplants.

In addition to impedance matching, couplant should also:
- conform closely to the test surface,
- be stable under test conditions,
- be noncorrosive — it should not react with the object, in bulk, or in crevices of the test object, and
- be easy to remove after testing.

Table 1: Test technique applications for basic product forms.

Product Form	Straight Beam	Angle Beam	Resonance Testing	Special Process	Reference Standard
Sheet	✓	✓	✓		Side-drilled hole, manufactured or ASME flat-bottom hole or notch
Plate	✓	✓			
Bar, billet	✓	✓			
Tube, pipe	✓	✓			
Casting	✓	✓		✓	Step wedge or natural
Braze, bond	✓		✓		Manufactured unbonded areas or pore
Weld	✓	✓		✓	Manufactured/ASME flat-bottom holes/notches, IIW, side-drilled holes (DAC)
Composite	✓	✓	✓	✓	Manufactured flat-bottom hole or notch

Pulse-Echo Techniques

Ultrasonic testing for discontinuities detection is most often performed using the pulse-echo technique. A single search unit is used for sending and receiving the ultrasound, as shown in Figure 1a. Short, uniformly timed pulses of ultrasound are transmitted into the test object and after the pulse is transmitted, the search unit is switched to a receiving circuit. When the ultrasound waves strike a discontinuity or boundary, some amount of the energy is reflected back toward the search unit and received by it. The use of the same unit for transmission and detection has advantages in terms of simplicity of inspection, as compared to using separate transmitting and receiving units for scanning the part. Another advantage, when compared to through transmission, is that inspection can be performed with access to only one side of the test piece.

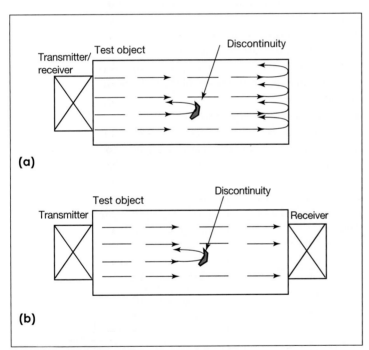

(a)

(b)

Figure 1: Ultrasonic test techniques: (a) pulse-echo technique; (b) through-transmission technique.

The major disadvantage of pulse-echo testing is that the initial (transmission) electric pulse saturates the detection circuitry and causes the transducer to *ring*; these factors create a time period when detection of reflected signals is impossible. The region of material directly below the surface that corresponds to this time period is called the *dead zone*. With modern search units and electronic circuitry, the dead zone can be kept quite small. With dual or multiple transducers, the dead zone can often be reduced.

Through-Transmission Technique

The through-transmission technique is also used for detecting discontinuities in an object. This technique requires two search units and access to opposite sides of the test piece. Ultrasonic waves are transmitted into the test object by a transmitting search unit. A receiving search unit is positioned on the test surface opposite the transmitting search unit to register the ultrasound passing through the object, as shown in Figure 1b. The amplitude of the signal transmitted through the test object is compared to the amount of the signal transmitted through a known discontinuity-free area, or through a reference material. A discontinuity or region of higher attenuation reduces the transmitted energy.

Contact Testing

Contact testing uses a thin film of couplant between the search unit (or the search unit shoe) and the test object. In addition to impedance matching, it is usually desirable that the couplant act as a lubricant so the search unit slides over the test surface easily, reducing wear on the contact face of the search unit. For this reason, oil, grease, or glycerin are the most common couplants used for contact tests. Maintaining sufficient coupling during movement of the search unit is a necessity, and requires care, particularly in the absence of relatively smooth test surfaces.

The search unit is scanned over the surface of the object, either manually or mechanically. To ensure complete testing of the desired region, it is necessary to move the search unit in such a way that successive passes overlap the previous path by a known, minimum amount. This overlap is usually specified in the test procedure, because it is necessary to account for beam spread and thereby ensure that each element of the object is searched by a suitably intense portion of the ultrasound beam.

A single search unit in pulse-echo mode is most commonly used, but multiple transducers (or multiple search units) in pitch catch or through-transmission mode may be used. Both straight beam and angle beam tests are common, and rayleigh or lamb waves may be used. When discontinuities near the test surface must be found, factors such as frequency, pulse length, and search-unit damping must be considered to optimize the near surface resolution.

Immersion Testing

In immersion testing, the test object is submerged in a liquid couplant, usually water, that contains a wetting agent and corrosion inhibitors suited to the materials to be tested. The couplant thickness amounts to a long, fluid delay line, which must be adjusted so that other signals do not interfere with reflections from within the object. As a result, it is not possible to test very thick materials. However, the technique is especially useful for testing objects with complex shapes that require several different angles of incidence of the sound beam, and mainte-nance of good coupling is seldom a problem. Also, continuously varying angles of incidence are possi-ble, which allows the proper angle of incidence of the beam to be maintained while following changes in surface geometry.

Both straight beam and mode converted angle beam tests are routinely performed, but surface waves are so rapidly attenuated by the couplant as to render them useless. Focused search units are often used in immersion testing to increase the test sensitivity in critical portions of the object. Either converging or diverging focus may be used depend-ing on the application. In many cases, suitable focusing can greatly reduce the effects of surface roughness.

Special Ultrasonic Testing Techniques

Some special ultrasonic testing techniques that are used include delta testing, tip diffraction, creeping waves, synthetic aperture focusing, ultrasonic tomography, acoustic microscopy, acoustic holog-raphy, and resonance testing.

Delta testing is an indirect, pitch catch test used primarily for weld metal. It is good for detecting discontinuities but has limited ability to determine their depth or size.

Tip diffraction is especially useful for sizing cracks, particularly the difficult depth or through wall dimension.

Creeping waves (fast surface waves) are useful for detecting small cracks at or near the surface, especially in dissimilar metal weld joints.

Synthetic aperture focusing technique and ultra-sonic tomography are computer-enhanced imaging techniques that detect and characterize discontinu-ities. Synthetic aperture focusing technique can produce images of discontinuities and ultrasonic tomography can be used to map stress concentra-tions.

Acoustic holography and microscopy are other techniques that can be used to produce images of discontinuities, the latter being most widely used with nonmetallics and electronic components.

Resonance testing, which is primarily used for material thickness gaging and bond testing, uses special ultrasonic testing equipment to determine the ultrasonic testing frequency at which the test material resonates.

Reference and Calibration Standards

To ensure accurate and repeatable inspection, ultra-sonic testing equipment must be standardized and calibrated so that data taken by different operators are comparable and can be matched against inspec-tion norms. This is accomplished through the use of reference and calibration standards or test blocks. Selection of a standard is determined by the testing technique, the material to be inspected and its form, the type of discontinuities to be detected, and the specification requirements.

Reference standards, such as those designed to ASTM, ASME, or AWS specifications, are used to standardize equipment responses. Blocks with flat-bottom holes (Figure 2) are often used to standard-ize the amplitude of the detected signal with respect to the effective area or distance of known reflectors. Area-amplitude or distance-amplitude curves are usually constructed using such blocks. In some cases, blocks with side-drilled holes are also used for such standardizations. Reference standards that

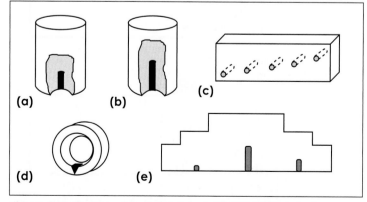

Figure 2: Reference blocks: (a) and (b) flat-bottom hole for area and distance amplitude blocks; (c) side-drilled holes; (d) known dimension notch; (e) flat-bottom holes in block manufactured from actual part.

vary acoustically from the test object by more than 6 dB are usually considered unacceptable for use.

Sometimes, it is preferable or required to prepare a reference standard from a piece of the same material as that to be tested, by introducing notches or holes into a sample or into the actual test object. The advantage of such a reference standard is that the test object and the standard will have the same composition, manufacturing history, surface condition, and geometry. The disadvantage is that usually there will be fewer artificial reflectors and it may not be possible to manufacture the reflectors as accurately as might be done with a separate standard. In this case, the piece of material selected must be scanned thoroughly to make sure it is discontinuity free.

Other types of standard test blocks (and some of the above reference blocks) are used to standardize the ultrasonic testing equipment with respect to essential variables such as sweep length, pulse energy and amplification, search unit characteristics, sensitivity, resolution, and linearity. Typical calibration blocks include IIW-type blocks, DC, SC, DSC, and MAB blocks. Two uses of the IIW-type blocks are shown in Figures 3a and b.

In all cases, standards must be prepared and used in strict accordance with well-designed specifications that cover the material, the fabrication, and the application of the blocks.

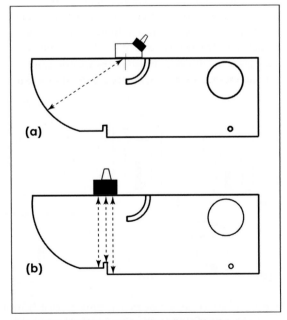

Figure 3: (a) IIW verification of angle beam search unit beam index point; (b) IIW determination of straight-beam depth resolution.

Inspection of Material Forms

Material forms commonly inspected by ultrasonic testing include ingots, pipe and tubular products, plate and sheet, bar and rod, forgings, castings, composites, welds, bonded structures, and special products.

Ingots

An ingot is refined material that is cast into a convenient shape for further processing into products such as bars, plate, and tubes. These intermediate forms may be further processed by hot or cold working, or machining to form the metal into a finished product.

Ultrasonic testing is usually performed on ingots to determine the location of discontinuities, such as pipe, cracks, gross porosity, or large inclusions that must be removed before further processing. Various ultrasonic testing techniques can be used to detect these discontinuities.

Immersion testing using large search units may be used for ultrasonic testing of square, round, or rectangular cross section ingots. Standard immersion may be used for smaller ingots, while water jets provide coupling for larger ingots. The pulse-echo technique is the most widely used.

Because ingots frequently have very rough surfaces, contact testing may be difficult. However, ingots too large for immersion testing are often contact tested and may be rough machined before testing to improve the reliability of the test.

In some metals such as nickel-based alloys, coarse grain structures can cause serious attenuation problems and reduce the effectiveness of ultrasonic testing.

Pipes and Tubular Products

Pipes and other tubular products are manufactured by various methods that include extrusion, swaging, drawing, forging, and welding. Typical discontinuities in nonwelded tube and pipe are gouges, seams, laps, eccentricity, and scabs. In welded products the discontinuities may be associated with the tube body or the weld. Discontinuities are usually associated with the weld joint, and are typically of the weld type, such as cracks, lack of penetration, porosity, and inclusions. Discontinuities associated with the pipe body in welded pipe are lamination and blisters.

Pipes and tubes are normally tested using the angle beam technique. Immersion testing is generally used for high volume testing. When the contact technique is used, the search units usually have curved shoes/wedges to conform to the pipe or tube surface. The frequency and beam angle used are selected to ensure detection of all relevant surface and subsurface discontinuities. The waves are propagated axially and circumferentially as shown in Figure 4 and should be moved in both axial and circumferential directions.

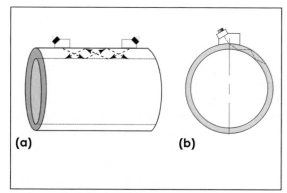

Figure 4: Angle-beam test in (a) axial and (b) circumferential directions.

Reference standards must have a wall thickness and outside diameter that are comparable to the test object. Therefore, it is common to prepare reference standards made from the material to be tested. Usually the artificial reflectors used are notches, with a depth of 3% to 5% of the wall thickness. Circumferential and axial notches are usually required, and should be located a minimum of 1 in. (25 mm) from the ends of the tube and separated by a sufficient distance to avoid spurious signals (Figure 5). Signals from the notches are usually set between 50% and 90% of full screen height to permit a common threshold for the inspection.

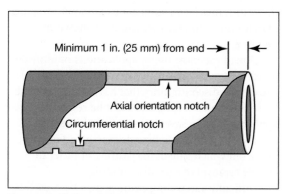

Figure 5: Piping/tubing reference standard.

Plate and Sheet

The primary forming process for steel is the continuous casting process in which molten steel is formed into slabs 8 in. to 12 in. (20.3 cm to 30.5 cm) thick, called *billets*. To a lesser extent, ingots are reheated and rolled into billets. (For more information on these processes, see *Ultrasonic Testing Classroom Training Book*, Chapter 8.) The cooled billets can then be reheated and passed through consecutively narrower sets of rolls to form plate or strip steel. For thinner sheet steel, the strip steel is cold-rolled (without reheating) to create thin sheet or foil. Lamination, scabs, seams, and edge cracks are the discontinuities usually sought by ultrasonic testing.

Plate may also be made by conventional casting, but this is normally done only for metals that tend to break up if rolled. The discussion of castings on page 22 applies to cast plate.

Rolled plate and sheet is usually ultrasonically inspected using straight beam or angle beam pulse-echo techniques. Both contact and immersion techniques can be used. Commonly, the material is tested by scanning from one side across the width or length of a single surface. An array of search units can be used for faster inspection and to ensure full coverage of the object. For critical applications, both straight beam and angle beam tests may be performed to increase the probability of detecting all relevant discontinuities regardless of their orientation and location.

Angle beam testing is much faster when 100% coverage is required, but laminations may remain undetected during inspection. Straight beam inspection cannot be performed on thin sheets when the front surface resolution does not allow the separation of the front surface from the back surface. A typical plate reference standard is shown in Figure 6.

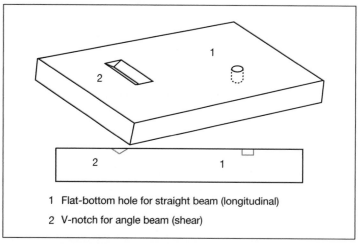

1 Flat-bottom hole for straight beam (longitudinal)

2 V-notch for angle beam (shear)

Figure 6: Plate reference standard.

An alternative inspection technique for suitable thicknesses of material uses lamb waves. Its use is not widespread but it is sometimes advantageous because full coverage of the width of the sheet can be obtained without moving the search unit across the sheet. However, the detected signal requires more complex signal processing because different frequency components propagate at different speeds.

Bar and Rod

Bar and rod stock are usually manufactured from billets by forging, drawing, extrusion, or rolling. In most cases, the working is done at elevated temperatures. Small bars may be cold drawn from larger bars and processed through a series of progressively smaller sized dies. Typical discontinuities include cracks, laps, seams, bursts, and in large-sized bars, may include flakes. Straight beam and angle beam pulse-echo techniques can be used for inspecting bar stock. Automated immersion systems can often reduce the time required for production inspections.

Bars are sometimes tested using a series of search units known as arrays. Figure 7 illustrates an array of two different search units mounted around the circumference of the bar stock. The bar is scanned by rotating it within the search units. With such systems, 100% coverage is obtained by using:

- Angle beam detection for surface and near surface discontinuities.
- Normal beam detection for deep-seated discontinuities.

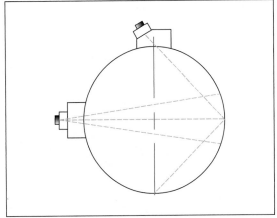

Figure 7: Bar stock search unit array.

Forgings

Forgings are manufactured by hammering or pressing ingots or billets into open or closed dies. It may be done hot or cold, but hot forging is most common. The open die process compresses the material between two flat anvils. The closed die process compresses the metal between contoured dies that surround the finished forging. Discontinuities that may occur include bursts, cold shuts, cracks, flakes, and laps.

Forgings are tested with contact or immersion techniques. Both straight beam and angle beam techniques are used, often on the same forging, because the test objects may be quite complex in shape. Because many forgings have rough surfaces, and the parts are frequently intended for critical service applications, it is often necessary to machine the test surface to ensure thorough test coverage and maximum sensitivity. For optimum results, the ultrasonic testing beam is generally directed at 90° to the direction of the principal metal flow that occurred during the forging process.

Castings

Castings are produced by pouring molten metal into simple- or complex-shaped molds. The sand casting process is used for large parts with relatively simple shapes that do not require close tolerances or smooth finishes, or that can be readily machined to required tolerances and finishes. Small parts, intricate shapes, and those requiring smooth surfaces and fine tolerances are produced by investment casting, shell casting, or permanent mold casting.

Straight beam inspections using contact, bubbler systems, or immersion are used to determine wall thickness, or to assist foundry personnel in locating hot tears, large shrinks, and similar serious discontinuities for process control. Sometimes, dual search unit techniques are useful as shown in Figure 8.

One of the most useful applications of ultrasonic testing for castings is to determine the depth of subsurface discontinuities that have been detected by radiographic testing and must be removed. This application often saves a great deal of time and money by establishing how deep to grind or chip, and from which side of the casting, in order to ensure removal of each discontinuity.

Difficulties in testing castings may be caused by the complex shapes that are often encountered and the relatively rough surfaces that are common. Castings of materials whose grain size cannot be refined by heat treatment, such as austenitic steels

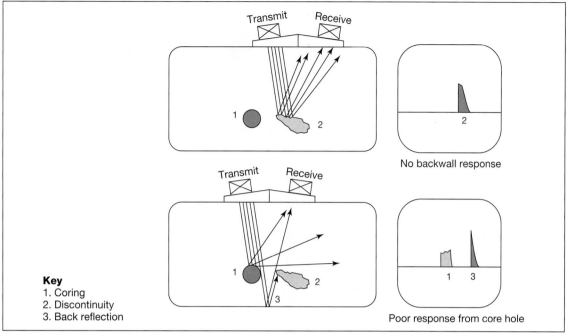

Figure 8: Ultrasonic testing signal response from dual search units in different positions on a casting section.

and nickel-base alloys, may have a very coarse grain structure that can cause severe testing problems. As described earlier, very high attenuation of the beam, coupled with severe ultrasonic noise, may be encountered. This situation requires the use of an ultrasound frequency that does not provide the required test sensitivity.

Typical discontinuities associated with castings include various kinds of shrinkage cavities, cold shuts, hot tears, cracks, gas or blow holes, porosity, inclusions, core shift, and unfused chaplets.

Composites

Composites are inhomogeneous materials usually consisting of layers of different materials that are bonded together or embedded in a matrix. Frequently, composites consist of layers of fiber with the fibers oriented in various directions. This situation causes major changes in ultrasonic properties in different portions of the laminate. Examples of composites that are ultrasonically tested include graphite/epoxy, glass/epoxy, and plastic/epoxy. Composites may also include layers of homogeneous materials such as aluminum sheet/glass epoxy.

Discontinuities that are commonly found in composites include delaminations, voids, porosity, and ply gaps. Voids and porosity are caused by outgassing of volatile chemical components in the

resin that are trapped during curing. They are typically located adjacent to the fibers in the matrix.

Delaminations can result from improper curing, but most are due to impact damage, hole drilling, or other sources of excess transverse tensile, or shear stresses. Delamination can also result from foreign material inclusions that contaminate layer surfaces during the lay up process.

Inclusions may be introduced from the ply carrier film, release paper, or peel plies, and they may be difficult to resolve due to low reflectivity. Ply gaps are caused by the misalignment of composite tapes during lay up and are difficult to detect because they are filled with resin during the processing of the composite.

The strength/life of a composite is seriously affected by delaminations or ply gaps in the composite structure. These planar discontinuities can propagate under normal service loads and result in component failure.

Composites are generally tested using a straight beam or through-transmission squirter technique at frequencies between 5 MHz and 25 MHz for materials less than 0.25 in. (6 mm). C-scans or digital computer imaging systems are often used for display and recording.

The integrity of the bond in adhesive bonded joints is determined by using commercially available bond testers. These machines use frequencies in the

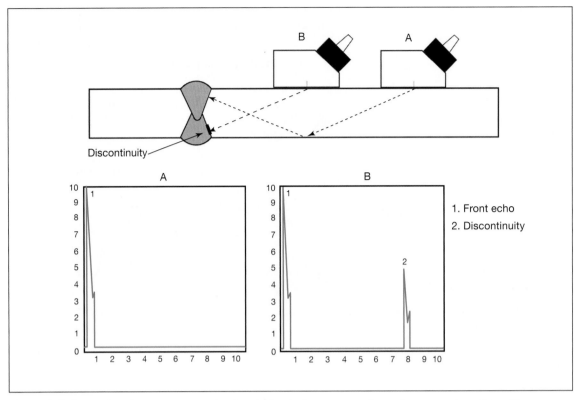

Figure 9: Pulse echo shear wave contact weld technique scan plan – two search unit positions.

range of 2.25 MHz to 25 MHz. The bond tester functions by transmitting a series of pulses into the material. Adhesive bond discontinuities are detected by comparing the signal amplitude of the ultrasound wave from the test piece to the ultrasound wave of a reference bond integrity standard. It is important that the reference standard resemble the test piece, especially in material composition and bond joint shape.

Reference standards are manufactured in nearly the same way as the test pieces. Delaminations and inclusions are simulated by implanting nonmetallic films in the reference standard to simulate the low reflectivity of foreign material discontinuities.

Welds

Welding processes widely used in manufacturing include electron beam, plasma arc, fusion, arc, spot, and resistance welding. Wrought and cast products are often joined using welding processes. All welding techniques, including automatic processes, are susceptible to discontinuities in the weld and in the adjoining base metal.

Manufacturing difficult assemblies and shapes requires the use of a variety of joint configurations. Common joint designs include variations of butt, fillet, and lap joints. Many different filler metals are used depending on the metals to be joined and

other variables in the process. Common weld discontinuities include hot cracks, cold cracks, porosity, inclusions, incomplete fusion, incomplete penetration, undercut, and melt through.

The ultrasonic shear wave contact technique with an A-scan presentation is most often used for detecting weld discontinuities, though immersion may be used for special applications. Generally, 2 MHz to 5 MHz is used for resolution of weld discontinuities. Higher frequencies up to 15 MHz are used on finer grained metals. An exact scan plan is necessary to ensure that all areas of the joint are evaluated. For example, in Figure 9, note that the ultrasound beam from the search unit in position (A) interrogates the weld, but will not be reflected from the discontinuity. When the search unit is moved to position (B), the discontinuity will be detected.

To ensure thorough testing of welded joints, the weld and the adjoining base metal must be searched in both longitudinal and transverse directions as shown in Figure 10. In addition, the base metal should be straight beam tested to protect against laminar discontinuities that would interfere with detection by the angle beam searches.

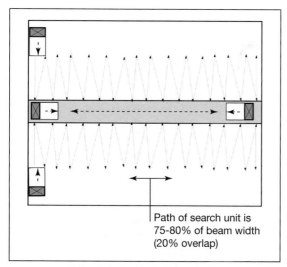

Figure 10: Search unit paths for full coverage of a ground flush plate weld.

Path of search unit is 75-80% of beam width (20% overlap)

Bonded Structures

Metallic brazing, soldering, and adhesive bonding are common types of bonding processes. Brazing and soldering use filler metals heated to temperatures above their melting point. Adhesive bonding uses adhesive (glue) to bond adjoining parts, usually metal sheets as shown in Figure 11. Typical discontinuities associated with bonding processes include incomplete fill, voids, base metal erosion (brazes only), lack of bond, and delamination.

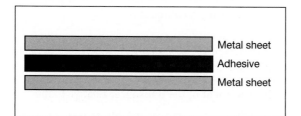

Metal sheet
Adhesive
Metal sheet

Figure 11: Adhesive bonding.

Bonded joints that cannot be usefully evaluated using radiographic testing can often be examined successfully with ultrasonic testing. Straight beam testing with frequencies between 5 MHz and 15 MHz usually produces good results in braze

inspections. Disbond, voids, and porosity can be detected. Ultrasonic testing braze standards often consist of a sample joint with a hole drilled to the interface surface or with a synthetic void made by using stop off tape to prevent entry of the filler material into portions of the joint, as shown in Figure 12.

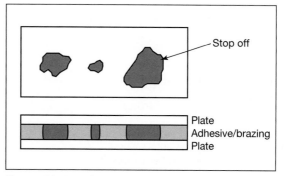

Stop off

Plate
Adhesive/brazing
Plate

Figure 12: Bond standard using stop off technique.

Special Products

Specialized pulse-echo techniques using attenuation and velocity measurements have been used successfully to examine wood, rubber, glass, and ceramic materials.

Wood, especially particleboard, is examined after hot processing using an array of air coupled search units. The technique uses a frequency of 30 kHz to 40 kHz to detect ply separations and other unfavorable discontinuities.

Rubber products are also tested with air coupled search units. Rubber used for automobile and aircraft applications is tested prior to recapping to ensure a sound rubber substrate.

Ultrasonic testing can resolve discontinuities on the order of 0.004 in. (0.1 mm) in ceramic and glass used in aerospace applications. Frequencies over 50 MHz are commonly used with focused search units. Due to the local density variations, microstructure, and surface conditions, ceramic and glass materials require specialized techniques and reference standards.

Review Questions

1. The ultrasonic testing technique that uses two search units is the:

   a. pulse-echo technique.
   b. through-transmission technique.
   c. resonance technique.
   d. angle beam technique.

2. The area at the front of a test object where discontinuities may be present but cannot be detected is called the:

   a. front zone.
   b. far field.
   c. dead zone.
   d. close field.

3. The technique commonly used to detect laminations located parallel to the surface of the test object is the:

   a. surface wave technique.
   b. straight beam technique.
   c. through-transmission technique.
   d. angle beam technique.

4. An advantage of the contact technique over the immersion technique is:

   a. the ability to scan irregularly shaped objects.
   b. better near surface resolution of discontinuities.
   c. deeper penetration power of sonic energy.
   d. that higher frequencies can be used for faster scanning.

5. In immersion angle beam testing of steel, the angle formed by the ultrasound beam and a line perpendicular to the component surface:

   a. increases when it penetrates the component and decreases when it leaves the component.
   b. decreases when it penetrates the component and increases when it leaves the component.
   c. decreases when it penetrates the component and decreases again when it leaves the component.
   d. increases when it penetrates the component and increases again when it leaves the component.

6. Couplant, used in contact testing, is a good conductor of sound waves and acts as a:

   a. noise suppressor.
   b. means to reduce the impedence between parts.
   c. means to reduce signal strength.
   d. source to reduce reflections from edges on the test object.

7. The primary difference between the contact and immersion testing techniques is:

   a. the use of oil couplant in immersion testing.
   b. the use of low-frequency search units in immersion testing.
   c. the placement of the transducer relative to the test piece.
   d. the use of two search units in immersion testing.

8. Standardization is defined as:

   a. indexing the search unit.
   b. adjusting the amplitude of the reflector.
   c. determining the proper sound entry angle.
   d. adjusting the ultrasonic testing equipment to a reference standard.

Answers

1b	2c	3b	4b	5a	6b	7c	8d

CHAPTER 4
Detection and Evaluation of Indications

Discontinuity Detection

Ultrasonic testing inspectors must have a thorough understanding of the ultrasonic testing process and its limitations to ensure that the appropriate test parameters are used. The inspector must know the typical discontinuities that may be found in an object manufactured in a particular manner, where they may lie in the object, and at what orientation. Proper identification of the test variables and selection of the equipment increases the probability of achieving an optimum test.

To obtain adequate sensitivity, the wavelength of the ultrasound and the transmitted signal amplitude must be properly chosen. It is generally believed that in contact testing (to be adequately reflected from a discontinuity) the wavelength of the sound must be no more than twice the smallest dimension (perpendicular to the beam) of the discontinuities to be detected. For a given material, test frequency can be increased to produce a shorter wavelength. In some situations, such as immersion testing with focused transducers, reliable detection of discontinuities smaller than 25% of the wavelength is possible. Sometimes, this requirement must be balanced against the ability to penetrate the object, which may require a longer wavelength (lower frequency). Similarly, the signal amplitude must be sufficient to produce indications from the discontinuities sought, but not so high as to allow common acceptable material characteristics to be mistaken for rejectable discontinuities.

The size, shape, type, orientation, and location of a discontinuity affect its ability to create ultrasonic reflections. Spherical discontinuities such as porosity reflect the least sound while smooth, flat discontinuities reflect the most. The type of discontinuity also determines the impedance mismatch — voids, such as cracks or porosity, have the most mismatch while bonded inclusions and some types of segregation have the least mismatch.

If the major reflecting portion of a discontinuity is not oriented at 90° to the ultrasonic beam, its maximum reflection will not be detected by a pulse-echo receiver. The reflector may be detected

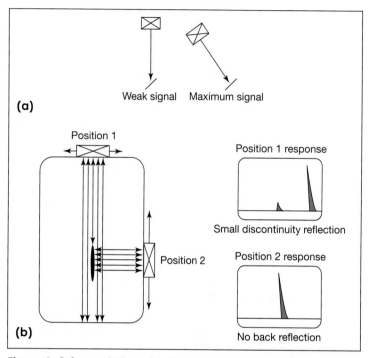

Figure 1: (a) angulation of search unit for maximum response; (b) testing from two surfaces to obtain maximum response.

at a lower amplitude, but the maximum amplitude could be found by using a different angle or by using a pitch-catch transducer arrangement and moving the receiver to maximize the response.

The inspection strategy, known as a scan plan, must be developed for each particular inspection. To provide an adequate inspection, the scan plan must take into consideration the material characteristics such as attenuation of the material, fabrication, and service history, along with possible damage mechanisms.

The beam angle(s) and scanning locations must be chosen to optimize the reflections from the expected discontinuities, as illustrated in Figure 1.

Search unit size must be selected so that the beam spread at the chosen test frequency will permit scanning the required portions of the object. Scan patterns must be chosen based on knowledge of the beam spread and regions to be inspected.

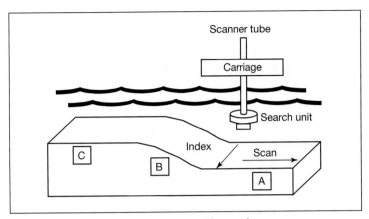

Figure 2: Immersion testing automatic carriage.

Figure 2 illustrates a typical immersion test setup on a forging that presents a few simple problems. A capable ultrasonic testing inspector must recognize that the thinner section (A) may require a different reference standard than the thicker section (C), and that the non-parallel area in section (B) will require a change in incident beam angle. It may also be beneficial to flip the object over and scan from the other surface.

A thorough understanding of the manufacturing or welding process is required to determine such factors as the type of discontinuities associated with the process, the normal orientation of these discontinuities, and the potential for interference from conditions such as coarse grain structures or component geometry. Given the many variables involved, it is usually advantageous to scan thoroughly from more than one direction, and often it is useful to use more than one wavelength or wave mode.

Evaluation of Indications

Depending on the application, industry, and applicable codes, the requirements to evaluate indications may vary greatly. Where some applications consider only the amplitude and location of a reflector to determine acceptability, others require the UT inspector to first determine the type of reflector and then, depending on the type of discontinuity, the physical dimensions of the reflector must be measured as accurately as practical.

Estimation of Discontinuity Size (Measurement of Maximum Amplitude)

In a typical A-scan test, ultrasound waves that are reflected from the test object back to the search unit are converted into electrical pulses. Their amplitude is represented by the height of the indication on the

display, while the distance (time) to the reflector is represented by the horizontal distance from the left side of the display to the indication.

Figure 3a illustrates a search unit on a reference block that is 2.5 in. (64 mm) from front to back, and contains a flat-bottom hole 0.5 in. (13 mm) deep. Figure 3b represents the A-scan display of the ultrasonic test shown in Figure 3a. The height of the indications represents the strength of the ultrasound reflections. The vertical scale on the display (Figure 4) is used to measure the signal amplitude as a percentage of screen height.

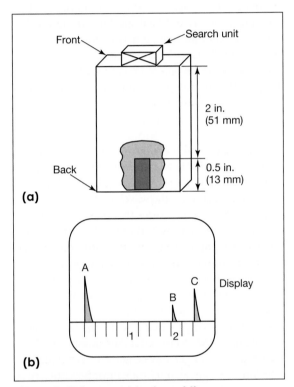

Figure 3: Reference block and the corresponding display.

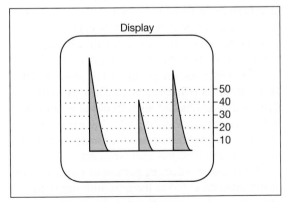

Figure 4: Vertical scale display.

Because the discontinuity may not be oriented optimally with reference to the beam direction, the search unit must be manipulated in order to determine the maximum indication amplitude that can be obtained from the discontinuity. With straight beams, this is done by scanning forward and backward, and side-to-side, in the general area where the indication was detected. With angle beams, the search unit is scanned back-and-forth and oscillated (rotated slightly clockwise and counter-clockwise) to try to get the sound beam perpendicular to the reflector. This should be done along the entire length of the discontinuity from all sides whenever possible.

Discontinuity sizing depends on whether an indication appears to have any length, width, or depth when scanning. This can be determined by noting the indication amplitude when moving the transducer left and right, or forward and backward. If the indication amplitude stays above a certain amplitude for some distance (usually greater than the beam spread at the indication sound path), then the indication can be said to have a certain length or width. The length or width is usually measured for most codes and standards by noting when the indication amplitude drops by 6 dB or 50% when moving away from the maximum amplitude point. This technique tends to oversize discontinuities that are not point discontinuities. Additional techniques to further characterize discontinuity size are noted at the end of this section.

A first approximation of discontinuity size or relevance for point reflectors when testing materials is usually made by comparing the maximum discontinuity indication with the indications from artificial reflectors in a reference standard. The indications that are compared must have been obtained with the same equipment and instrument settings. Because the amplitude of reflections varies with both the distance from reflector to search unit and the area of the reflector, many codes and standards rely on a distance-amplitude curve (DAC) constructed using reference reflectors of a single size. The amplitude of discontinuity reflection is compared with that of a reference reflector of the same size at that distance, as determined by the DAC. It is a common requirement to further evaluate any reflector whose amplitude is as great as 20% of DAC (14 dB below the DAC) to determine its maximum amplitude. This method is typically used in angle-beam inspections and followed by a separate procedure to determine the length and sometimes the vertical extent of the discontinuity.

For other applications an area-amplitude curve made with reference reflectors of differing sizes is used for comparison. This is often used with straight-beam examinations, and there may be area-amplitude references with one or more additional reflector depth used. Distance-amplitude curves for multiple reflector sizes may thus be generated. The discontinuity indication is compared with these curves to estimate the discontinuity size or amplitude.

American Welding Society (AWS) structural welding codes rely on specific formulas and tables for angle-beam weld examinations that take into account attenuation effects and decibel differences from reflectors to determine acceptability of discontinuities. This is possible because the code specifies the transducer frequency and dimensions, and applies to a specific type of material. These limitations determine the length of the near field and approximate beam spread, so attenuation can be taken as a constant (2 dB per inch after the first inch of sound path in structural steel). This eliminates the need to construct a distance-amplitude curve and a single side-drilled hole is used to determine the reference level. This is accomplished by inputting the discontinuity indication information (sound path, reference level decibel, and indication level decibel) into a formula that provides the inspector with an indication rating. This rating is then input into the correct section of a table based on material thickness, and results in a classification of the indication. Each class has different acceptability limits that are based on the overall length of the indication and its proximity to other discontinuities. This formula cannot be used for examination of other materials, or with transducers of other frequencies and/or dimensions.

The estimated discontinuity sizes found in these ways are almost always smaller than the actual discontinuity sizes. This is true because discontinuities usually are not as efficient reflectors as flat-bottom or through holes, due to factors such as orientation, surface roughness, impedance, or shape of the discontinuity. For example, in a large steel forging, a 2 in. × 3 in. (50 mm × 76 mm) silicate inclusion produced an indication smaller than that from a 0.06 in. (1.6 mm) flat-bottom hole at the same distance. The small reflection was primarily a result of a good impedance match between the discontinuity and the steel, because the silicate was bonded to the steel. Other types of discontinuities that could cause the same result include smooth, spherical discontinuities such as porosity, discontinuities that taper to undetectable dimensions at their ends, and cracks that twist so that part of their length is edgewise to the beam.

Occasions when flat-bottom hole data overestimate the discontinuity size are rare. They usually involve discontinuities that are concave relative to the incident beam and are located so that the reflection is focused at the receiving search unit.

Other means of assessing discontinuity size include discontinuity mapping techniques such as signal drop (decibel drop), phased array, time of flight diffraction, and special techniques such as creeping wave, bi-modal, and tip diffraction where an attempt is made to get a signal from the tip of a discontinuity to measure the actual size of the discontinuity regardless of the amplitude.

Evaluation of Signal Patterns

The shape and width of a reflected signal on the display can suggest the type of discontinuity causing the reflection, but should not be considered 100% accurate. This information is subjective and assumes that the technique has maximized the ultrasound reflection and that the reflector has a simple, regular shape. Figure 5 illustrates possible signal responses from a crack-type discontinuity as an angle-beam probe is moved so that the discontinuity intercepts first the leading edge, then the

center, and finally the trailing edge of the beam. There are a number of clues that can be observed when performing an angle-beam examination.
- Shape of the signal.
- Change in signal when testing from the opposite direction such as the opposite side of the weld from the same test surface (Figure 6).
- Change in the signal as the probe is swiveled (Figure 7).
- Change in the signal as the probe is moved parallel to an elongated indication.
- Surface location of the indication.
- Width of the indication.
- Signal amplitude (Figure 8).
- Vertical projection of the reflector.

Figure 9 shows the displays from two immersion tests. The response from a straight beam test shows a strong front surface pulse, the discontinuity, and a back reflection. The angle beam test shows only the discontinuity and the corner reflections. If the front surface is smooth, it may provide no indication at all, as shown in the case of Figure 9b.

When performing inspections on components that have been in service, it is important to identify the type of reflector. To properly evaluate reflectors, the characteristics of the component in the area of the indication must be known. This may require scanning the area with a straight beam transducer

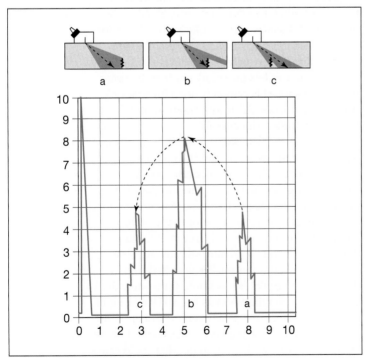

Figure 5: Signal display of indications.

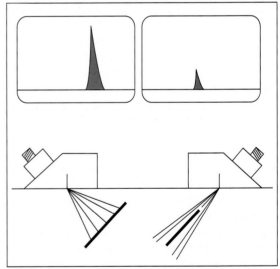

Figure 6: Scanning from the opposite direction may cause a change in signal.

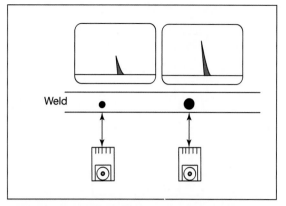

Figure 8: Signal amplitude is an indication of discontinuity size. Larger discontinuities reflect more sound than smaller but similar discontinuities.

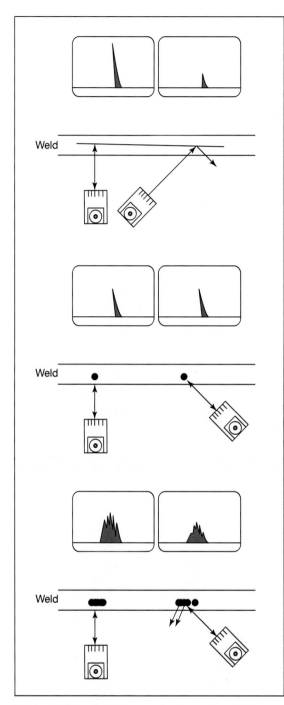

Figure 7: The signal may change when the probe is swiveled.

to measure the thickness so the indication location can be determined relative to the inside surface. Components such as storage tanks or vessels may have welded attachments, grinding areas, or gouges on the inside. These fabrication artifacts can produce indications that may look like a relevant discontinuity. Without properly evaluating the component, changes in geometry or fabrication artifacts could mistakenly be reported as relevant discontinuities.

Figure 10 shows what a shear wave inspection of a weld could look like. With the transducer in position 1 an indication is detected. To determine if the reflector is at location A or B, the inspector should verify the reflector from the other side of the weld, as seen at position 2. The inspector should also interrogate the area with a straight beam to see if there are any changes in geometry in the area which could be indicated by a change in thickness or a loss in backwall due to the unfavorable geometry of the fillet weld.

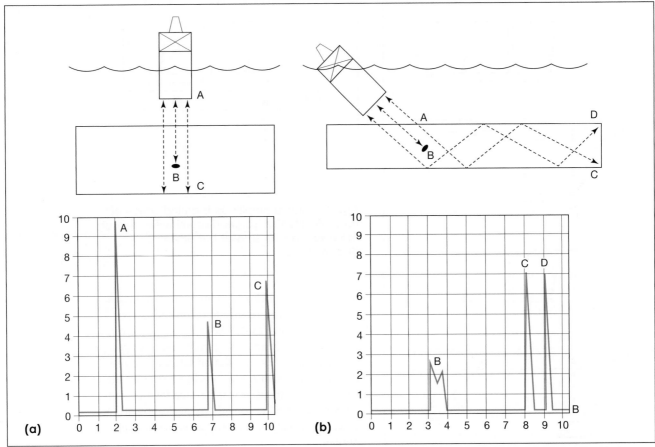

Figure 9: Response display from (a) an immersion straight beam compared to the display from (b) an angle beam.

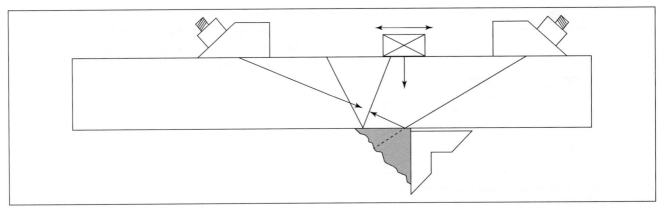

Figure 10: An example of a shear wave inspection of a weld.

Review Questions

1. Of the options below, what are two key factors to consider when attempting to detect small reflectors?

   a. The distance after the reflector and ratio of velocity to amplitude.
   b. The wavelength and the transmitted signal amplitude.
   c. The shape of the discontinuity and the distance after the reflector.
   d. The wavelength of the discontinuity type and the shear to longitudinal ratio.

2. A reference standard is:

   a. used to set the inspection sensitivity to a known standard size reflector.
   b. the code of record for the item being inspected.
   c. made of aluminum and is primarily used to set the wavelength of the inspection system.
   d. made of steel and is primarily used to set the wavelength of the inspection system.

3. To be reflected from a discontinuity, the wavelength of the sound must be:

   a. no less than two times the smallest dimension.
   b. no less than two times the largest dimension.
   c. no more than two times the smallest dimension.
   d. no more than two times the largest dimension.

4. When trying to determine the maximum amplitude of an indication, which of the following factors need to be considered?

   a. The orientation of the discontinuity related to the sound beam.
   b. The wavelength and the transmitted signal amplitude.
   c. The ratio of longitudinal velocity to shear velocity.
   d. The wavelength of the discontinuity type and the shear to longitudinal ratio.

5. Of the options below, which answer represents the most important factors to consider when developing a scan plan to obtain the best inspection?

   a. The time allotted to perform the inspection, the access to the item, and the material.
   b. The angle of the transducer available for the inspection, the thickness of the material, and the time allotted for the inspection.
   c. The type of discontinuity expected, the geometry in the area to be inspected, and the beam angles required to detect the expected discontinuities.
   d. The wavelength of the expected discontinuity, the area to be inspected, and the transducer available for the inspection.

6. When comparing the amplitude of a discontinuity to the reflector in a reference block:

   a. if the amplitude is the same, then the physical dimension of the discontinuity is the same as the reference reflector.
   b. the material the block is made of does not have to be the same as long as the amplitude matches.
   c. the material and the distance to the reflector have an impact on the amplitude.
   d. you can record the amplitude from the reference reflector with one transducer and compare it to the amplitude found with a different transducer optimized for the indication.

7. When attempting to determine the type of discontinuity causing an indication:

   a. the type of discontinuity does not matter unless the amplitude is two times greater than the reference reflector.
   b. the signal pattern and geometry in the area of the indication should be evaluated.
   c. the type of discontinuity cannot be determined with ultrasonic testing.
   d. the wavelength analysis of the discontinuity is used to determine the discontinuity type.

8. When attempting to detect very small discontinuities:

   a. a lower frequency will typically be able to detect smaller discontinuities.
   b. for a given material and frequency, a larger transducer will find smaller discontinuities.
   c. the angle at which the sound intersects the discontinuities does not matter.
   d. a higher frequency will typically be able to detect smaller discontinuities.

Answers

1b   2a   3c   4a   5c   6c   7b   8d

CHAPTER 5
Time of Flight Diffraction

History

Dr. Maurice Silk developed time of flight diffraction (TOFD) in the early 1970s at the National NDT Centre in Harwell, UK.

Originally developed as a sizing technique, it consists of stacked A-scans and grayscale images. The first practical examination was developed during the 70s and a number of successful trials were developed in the 80s, making TOFD an acceptable ultrasonic testing technique.

Further advancements in computer software led to the development of parabolic cursors, the removal and straightening of the lateral wave, and the use of the synthetic aperture focusing technique (SAFT).

Theory

A basic TOFD technique uses a single set of pitch-catch probes: one transmitter (Tx) and one receiver (Rx), shown in Figure 1.

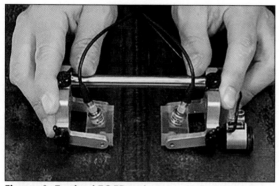

Figure 1: Typical TOFD set up.

TOFD may be used with immersion, contact, or gap techniques. Single element or phased array piezoelectric probes may be used. Because of the need for probes with heavy damping, most phased array probes do not make good TOFD probes.

Electromagnetic acoustic transducers (EMAT) or other nonstandard probes may be used with qualification.

TOFD uses refracted compression (longitudinal) waves to perform examinations. Longitudinal waves are used because of their increased beam spread (approximately twice that of shear waves) and the lack of mode conversions in the initial signal.

The diffracted signals from a discontinuity are received via the receiver probe and are evaluated using an ultrasonic B-scan image side view, sometimes called a D-scan.

Advantages and Disadvantages of TOFD

When evaluating a TOFD inspection, a reference is made using the lateral wave response. The depth to the indications is calculated from the difference in the time of flight between the lateral wave and the diffracted pulse.

For critical discontinuity sizing, the probes must be repositioned or additional probes added so that the discontinuities are situated directly between the probes.

Other techniques, such as using different angles (one 45°, one 70°) in the same TOFD pair of probes or tandem probes, may also be used to help locate discontinuities when using TOFD.

Because TOFD is based on diffracted ultrasonic waves instead of on reflected ultrasonic waves, the angular position of the discontinuity has very little effect on the detection of the discontinuity.

Advantages of TOFD
- The potential to have an accuracy of within ±1 mm in sizing.
- Less sensitive to discontinuity orientation.
- Greater penetrating ability.
- B-scan imaging.
- Accurate sizing capability.
- Fast.
- Easy interpretations of mid-wall indications.
- When monitoring discontinuity growth, it becomes more accurate with repeatability within 0.01 in. (0.3 mm).

Disadvantages of TOFD

- Poor detection/sizing near the entry and backwall surfaces.
- Requires an additional scan to approximate on which side of the weld the discontinuity is located.
- Optimum probe center spacing may result in probe interference with weld cap.
- Mismatch (high, low) conditions may mask root discontinuities in the backwall signal of welds.
- Weak signals.
- Sensitive to material grain noise.
- Inspection surface curvature can increase existing dead zones.

How TOFD Works

When ultrasound strikes a discontinuity, diffraction takes place at its extremities, or tips, in addition to the normal reflected wave. These waves radiate 360° from the tip. (See Figure 2.) It is the diffracted waves from the extremities that are used in TOFD.

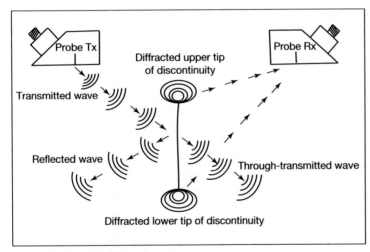

Figure 2: How TOFD works.

The orientation of the discontinuity is less critical in TOFD than in conventional pulse echo ultrasonic inspection.

In addition to energies diffracted by discontinuities, TOFD also detects a lateral wave at the surface traveling directly between the probes (Figure 3). The lateral wave is longitudinal and will exist as long as the required beam spread is achieved.

Also included in the TOFD image are the backwall echoes created from the wave that reaches the far side of the test piece without interference from any discontinuity. Discontinuities may be lost in the backwall reflections.

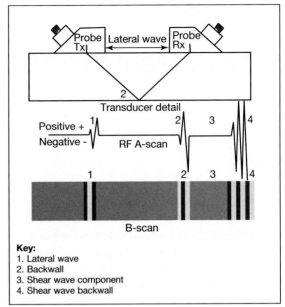

Key:
1. Lateral wave
2. Backwall
3. Shear wave component
4. Shear wave backwall

Figure 3: TOFD image radio frequency A-scan and grayscale B-scan.

In addition, a shear-wave component and shear-wave backwall are generated (Figure 3). This shear-wave component contains useful information and should be visible on the display during inspection and evaluation.

Determining the Location of a TOFD Discontinuity

A lack of near-surface and far-surface resolution coverage exists in all TOFD inspections. This is caused by loci of the ultrasonic beam at the near surface of the lateral wave or upper loci, and at the far surface (backwall) or lower loci (Figure 4) of the test specimen, and the ringing time of the transducer crystal.

These loci may cause some or all of a signal from the discontinuity to be lost. In addition, a discontinuity may be lost if located outside the ultrasonic beam in the dead zone.

Along with determining length and depth of the indication, we can determine if the discontinuity is inside diameter (ID) or outside diameter (OD) connected, or fully embedded in the volume of the part. This is determined by evaluating the phase transformation or phase shift of the signal from the discontinuity.

In a scan without a discontinuity, the lateral wave display (Figure 3) appears as a positive-negative-positive in the RF A-scan and black-white-black in the grayscale B-scan. The phase shift of the backwall of a scan without a discontinuity will be opposite of

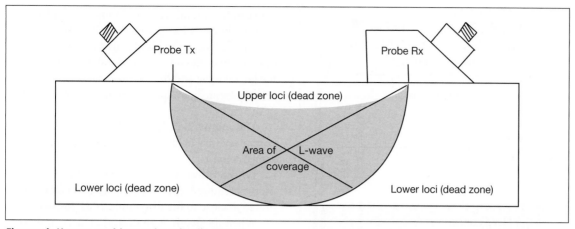

Figure 4: Upper and lower longitudinal loci.

the lateral wave negative-positive-negative in the RF A-scan or white-black-white in the grayscale image.

When a fully embedded discontinuity is detected, phase transformation occurs (Figure 5). The upper tip of the indication will be opposite of the lateral wave, so it will appear negative-positive-negative in the RF A-scan or white-black-white, or the same as the backwall as shown in Figure 5. The lower tip of the indication phase shift will be the positive-negative-positive, or black-white-black, or the same as the lateral wave.

Discontinuities that do not show this type of phase change are considered to be either ID or OD connected. The upper phase change is hidden in the lateral wave, or the lower phase change is hidden in the backwall signal.

Outside diameter connected discontinuities (Figure 6) do not show a phase change; therefore, their responses appear the same as the lateral wave positive-negative-positive in the RF A-scan and black-white-black in the B-scan grayscale.

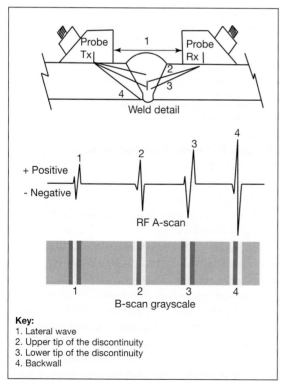

Figure 5: Fully embedded discontinuity.

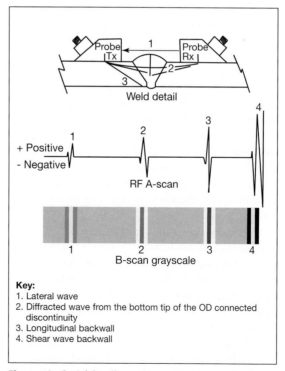

Figure 6: Outside diameter connected TOFD indication.

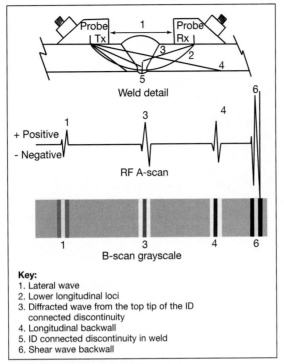

Figure 7: Inside diameter connected discontinuity.

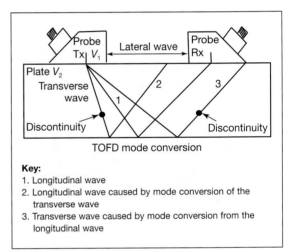

Figure 8: Shear wave component.

between the lateral wave and longitudinal backwall thickness is located halfway in depth of the part thickness. A visually located discontinuity one-eighth of the way in the visual image between the lateral wave and the longitudinal backwall is actually located one-quarter of the way in the depth of the part.

The approximate height of any additional discontinuity may be quickly estimated by using the same method.

When critical sizing and depth of the discontinuity is required, the TOFD image should be calibrated as close to the discontinuity as possible.

When the depth of an indication is critical, the probes should be repositioned so that the discontinuity is located directly in the middle of the TOFD probes.

The shear wave component (Figure 8) is made up of refracted shear waves caused by Snell's law as the longitudinal and shear wave beams strike the backwall of the test specimen at an angle other than normal.

Because the shear waves are slower, they show up later in time than the longitudinal backwall. The shear wave component is located lower in the display than the backwall.

The shear wave component contains important information about the location of discontinuities used during the evaluation of a TOFD image.

Discontinuities viewed between the lateral wave and backwall may or may not be visible in the shear wave component; it is dependent on the location of the discontinuity between the probes.

Indications that are in the shear wave components are normally those that are off-center of the probe centerline.

With inside diameter (ID) connected discontinuities (Figure 7), the lateral wave is positive-negative-positive in the RF A-scan, and black-white-black in the grayscale B-scan.

The ID connected top produces a phase change and appears in the negative-positive-negative RF A-scan and white-black-white in the B-scan grayscale. Because the bottom of the discontinuity is located inside the backwall, there is no phase change visible as the top of the indication and the backwall appear the same.

Note: Not all indications display these phase changes. If a discontinuity height is less than the ringing time of the signal or <0.1 in. (3 mm), then it will not be possible to differentiate the top and bottom signals; therefore, no phase change may be visible.

The B-scan grayscale depth display in TOFD is logarithmic and not linear; therefore, a discontinuity does not appear in the correct position in depth when viewed on the display. Because TOFD is logarithmic and not linear, the deeper in the part that the discontinuity is located, the better the resolution.

A discontinuity located in the grayscale image, directly halfway between the lateral wave and the longitudinal backwall, is actually located three-fourths of the depth of the part thickness, while a visually located discontinuity one-quarter of the way

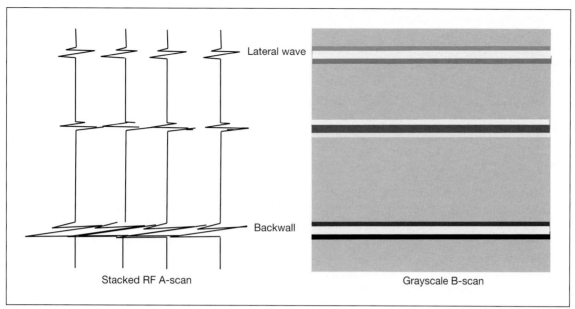

Lateral wave

Backwall

Stacked RF A-scan

Grayscale B-scan

Figure 9: Stacked RF A-scan and B-scan grayscale.

Grayscale Image

There are two views used for TOFD inspections: the RF A-scan waveform presentation and the B-scan grayscale image.

The TOFD B-scan display provides a sectional view of the weld with a minimum of 64 grayscale levels and is made up of stacked A-scans (Figure 9).

Caution: Do not use color B-scan displays for a TOFD display. Color displays (Doppler images) are intended for use in amplitude-based inspection, and may cause crack-like indications to be missed, and/or will enhance the ability to detect porosity, giving the inspector a false sense that the inspection display is correct.

Because the receiving transducers receive the diffracted ultrasound and not the reflected sound, as in pulse-echo ultrasonic inspection, the exact location of a discontinuity between probes is not known. All that can be determined is that the discontinuity is somewhere between the transmitter and receiver probes of the TOFD probe pair.

Equipment

Probes, Wedges, Preamps, and Encoders

Probes
TOFD probes are made of composite materials and are highly dampened. Most TOFD probes are single-element longitudinal probes. (See Figure 10.)

Figure 10: TOFD probe.

Phased array probes typically do not have the dampening required to be used as TOFD probes.

Like conventional ultrasonic inspections for thin material, high-frequency, small-diameter probes are typically used. For thick materials, lower frequency probes are used. The wavelength of a TOFD inspection, and therefore its sensitivity, can be calculated using the basic wavelength formula in Equation 1.

(Eq. 1) $\lambda = \dfrac{V}{f}$

where
    λ is wavelength of the ultrasonic beam,
    V is velocity of the material being inspected, and
    f is frequency of the ultrasonic transducer.

Note: The smallest discontinuity that can be located by an ultrasonic test is one-half the wavelength.

Beam spread is another important factor in choosing a TOFD probe because the beam spread determines the amount of coverage in the TOFD inspection area. The half-beam spread may be calculated by:

(Eq. 2) $$\sin \gamma = \frac{1.22\lambda}{D}$$

where

γ is half beam angle in degrees,
λ is wavelength of the ultrasound, and
D is diameter of the transducer.

The main effect of beam spread on a TOFD inspection is the coverage of the inspection area.

Focused or unfocused probes may be used to perform TOFD inspection. Unfocused probes are recommended for detection, and focused probes may be used to improve resolution for sizing.

The typical TOFD single-element probe sizes are 1/4 in. to 3/8 in. (6.35 mm to 9.53 mm) in diameter.

Small probes produce greater beam spread; therefore, they provide greater coverage of the weld or part. (See Equation 2.)

When single-element probes are used, rounded probes are preferred over square probes because they produce fewer side lobes causing less noise.

The typical frequency range for TOFD inspection is from 5 MHz to 20 MHz. (See Table 1.) The actual frequency used depends on the part thickness, type of material to be inspected, and the sensitivity and inspection coverage required. This is similar to conventional pulse-echo ultrasonic inspections.

In some cases, a frequency as low as 2 MHz may be required for certain types of stainless steel materials.

Common requirements for TOFD probes:
- A minimum of two probes must be used in a pitch-catch arrangement.
- Each probe in the pair shall have the same nominal frequency.
- The pair shall have the same element dimensions.
- The pulse duration of the probe shall not exceed 2 cycles as measured to the 20 dB level below the peak response of the probe.

Wedges

The incident angle and refracted angles used in TOFD should be selected to provide the required coverage. This coverage is based on Equation 3 called Snell's law (Figure 11).

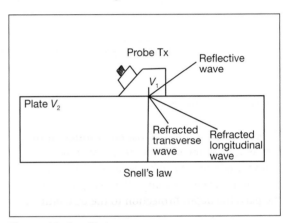

Figure 11: Snell's law.

(Eq. 3) $$\frac{\sin \theta_1}{\sin \theta_2} = \frac{V_1}{V_2}$$

where

θ_1 is angle of the probe,
θ_2 is refracted angle in the plate,
V_1 is velocity in the wedge, and
V_2 is velocity of the material inspected.

TOFD wedges can be made of acrylic, polystyrene microwave plastic, or other common ultrasonic wedge material. These wedges are cut on an index angle to produce the longitudinal refracted wave (Figure 12).

When calculating angles for TOFD inspections, remember to use the longitudinal incident and refracted angle. Use the longitudinal velocity as both V_1 (the velocity in the wedge) and V_2 (the velocity in the part to be inspected).

Table 1: Recommended probe.

Nominal Wall Thickness in. (mm)	Nominal Frequency (MHz)	Element Size in. (mm)	Recommended Angles (Degrees)
<0.5 (12)	10 to 15	0.08 to 0.25 (2 to 6)	60 to 70
0.5 to 1.4 (12 to <35)	5 to 10	0.08 to 0.25 (2 to 6)	50 to 70
1.4 < 2.9 (35 to <75)	2 to 5	0.25 to 0.5 (6 to 12)	45 to 65

Figure 12: Typical TOFD wedge for 70° longitudinal wave TOFD inspections.

Most TOFD wedges have wear pins or plates made of carbide or steel inserted inside the wedges. The wear plate/pin reduces the amount of wear on the softer wedge material. Worn wedges can lead to a change of inspection angle and inaccuracy in depth measurements.

Wedge delay — the time it takes for the ultrasound to travel through the wedge — is an important factor in calibrating the TOFD system. The velocity of the wedge is most likely different from the velocity of the material being inspected. Without taking into account the time it takes for the sound to travel through the wedge and into the part, the depth projection to the discontinuity cannot be correct.

Two different angles may be used in a pair of TOFD probes. As an example, a 60° angle may be used to transmit, and a 45° angle may be used to receive. Using different transmitting and receiving angles, the area of coverage will change.

Connectors

Various connectors are used to connect the probes to preamplifiers and preamplifiers to the unit. TOFD connectors may be phased array, push-pull connectors, RF connectors, coaxial and multi-pin connectors, or a combination (Figure 13).

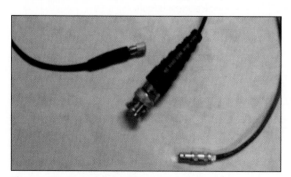

Figure 13: Typical TOFD connectors.

Preamplifiers

Because TOFD signals are weak, preamplifiers are sometimes required (Figure 14). Most preamps operate at a frequency ranging from 500 Hz to greater than 50 MHz, increasing gain between 30 dB and 60 dB.

Figure 14: TOFD preamplifier.

Encoders

Encoders used in TOFD work by an optical or magnetic sensor (hall effect). The encoders are connected to the instrument by an electrical cable.

TOFD scans may be performed with or without an encoder; however, encoding is required when recording the discontinuity position and length in the scan axis (direction of scanning).

When the encoder is moved, the pulser circuit in the unit pulses the element inside the transducer. If the encoder slips or does not move, then there will be gaps (skips) in the data. Codes and standards restrict the amount of skips (lost data) allowed in a scan when using an encoder.

Instrument

TOFD instruments may be portable or computer-based and often use software to aid in the setup and evaluation of TOFD scans (Figure 15).

Onboard software allows for the evaluation of the scans on the unit and may allow for transfer and removal of scan data by disk for further evaluation on a computer (Figures 16, 17, and 18).

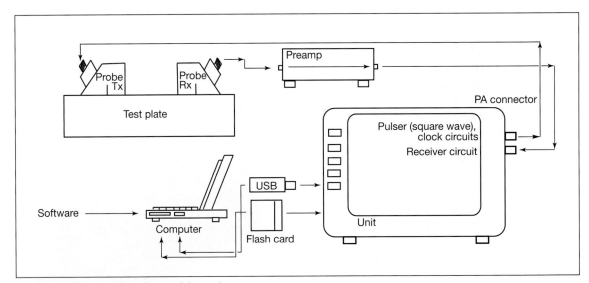

Figure 15: Schematic of portable system.

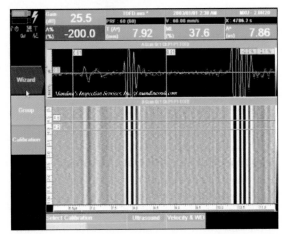

Figure 16: Unit display with onboard software.

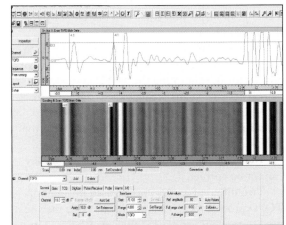

Figure 17: Computer software display.

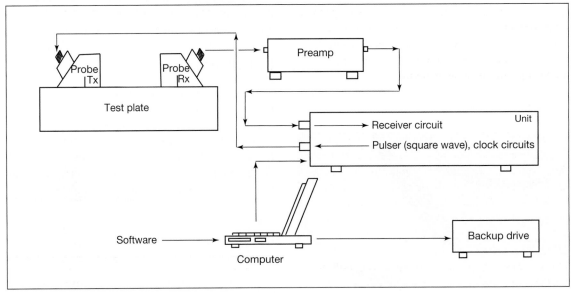

Figure 18: Schematic of computer-operated system.

Processors

Standards require that the ultrasonic instrument's pulser provide unipolar or bipolar square waves.

The pulse width should be tunable to allow optimization of pulse amplitude and duration.

The normal element ring time for probes is 1 to 1.5 cycles, but no more than 2 cycles.

The bandwidth of the ultrasonic receiver shall be at least equal to that of the nominal probe frequency and such that the –6 dB bandwidth of the probe does not fall outside of the –6 dB bandwidth of the receiver probe.

The receiver gain control should be able to adjust the signal amplitude in increments of 1 dB or less.

The time and amplitude linearity of a TOFD unit is ±5% of the actual full-scale amplitude.

Analog to digital conversion of waveforms should have sampling rates at least four times that of the nominal frequency of the probe. When digital signal processing is to be carried out on the raw data, the processing is increased to eight times the nominal frequency of the probe.

Instrument Settings

TOFD uses signal averaging to reduce electrical noise. Normal averaging settings are eight or 16. Averaging decreases the amount of noise (hash) in a TOFD inspection.

Note: Averaging does not reduce noise from large grains from the material or weld metal.

For material up to 2 in. (5 cm) thick, the maximum pulse repetition rate that may be used is 1500 pulses per second.

The use of bandpass filtering changes the sensitivity and resolution of the examination. The addition of a broad filtering will reduce the detectability of the examination and discontinuities may be missed.

Caution: Filter settings should be used with care. Excessive high- and low-pass filtering may cause indications to be missed.

Software

Computer-based systems provide additional functions that may be used as tools in the evaluation of TOFD images. These include straightening of lateral wave and removal of the lateral wave and backwall. The use of the synthetic aperture focusing technique (SAFT) and hyperbolic cursors are other common TOFD software tools.

Straighten Lateral Wave and Backwall

During scanning, and as the probe travels, both the backwall and the lateral wave may produce excessive wavy scans. The inspector may straighten the lateral wave or the backwall to aid in the evaluation process.

Both the lateral wave and backwall may be straightened using TOFD software tools (Figure 19). The TOFD scan should always be evaluated prior to the straightening of the lateral wave or backwall. It is important to note that when straightening the lateral wave or backwall a loss of valuable information could occur.

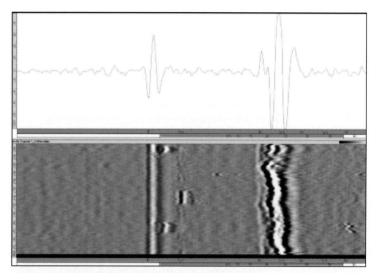

Figure 19: Straightening of the lateral wave.

Removal of Lateral Wave and Backwall

Removal of the lateral wave may be used to resolve near surface indications that are not outside diameter (OD) connected (Figure 20). Lateral wave removal occurs through simple mathematical subtraction of stored data points.

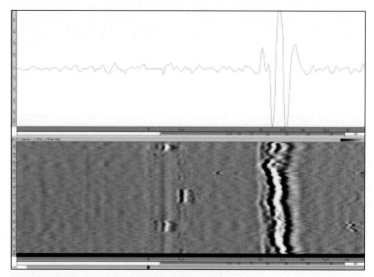

Figure 20: Scan with lateral wave removed.

The amplitude of the discontinuity, and the time at which it arrives, affect the use of this software function.

Variation in couplant thickness affects both the location (time shift) and amplitude of a discontinuity and may reduce the effectiveness of the lateral removal software function.

Because the lateral wave is removed, the measurements may lack the accuracy of measurements taken using the lateral wave.

If possible, the lateral wave should be removed only in the area required, so that the adjoining area may be used to measure the depth and size of the discontinuities using the lateral wave as reference.

Synthetic Aperture Focusing Technique

The synthetic aperture focusing technique algorithms of time domain (TD-SAFT) and frequency domain (FD-SAFT) are used to enhance the quality of the scan image. SAFT creates a relatively clear image obtained using algorithms (Figure 21).

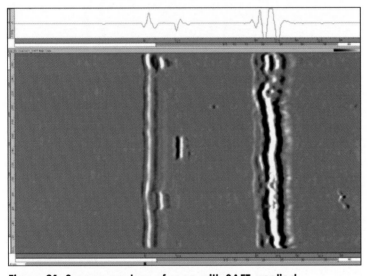

Figure 21: Screen capture of scan with SAFT applied.

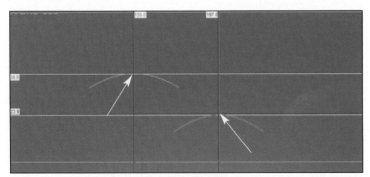

Figure 22: Hyperbolic measuring cursors.

SAFT processing enhances the lateral resolution of the TOFD image and is helpful in distinguishing small discontinuities.

Hyperbolic Cursors

The most commonly used software tool is the hyperbolic cursor. TOFD transducers gain energy as the leading edge contacts the leading edge of a discontinuity. This energy peaks and then loses energy as it passes the end of the discontinuity (Figure 22).

Because of the rise and fall of this energy level at the beginning and end of the discontinuity, the TOFD indication in the display (B-scan) turns down.

Measuring the indication at its end (and not where it turns down) will result in oversizing the indication's length.

To measure the length of an indication, hyperbolic cursors turn down at the ends of the indication and increase discontinuity length measurement accuracies.

Setting up a TOFD Inspection

There are two TOFD displays: the RF A-scan and B-scan grayscale.

The RF A-scan should be used for setup and calibration of the TOFD system, as well as sizing the depth and height of discontinuities. The B-scan is used to determine the type of discontinuities that have been detected.

Setting up the Display for TOFD

To set up a simple TOFD inspection, perform the following.

Step 1: Calculate the probe center spacing (PCS); the distance between the probe's exit points.

Step 2: Space the probes. (Use the exit points on the wedges.)

Step 3: Place the probes on the part.

Step 4: In the RF display, place the lateral wave at a minimum of 1 µs prior to the lateral wave and include the backwall and shear wave component.

Step 5: Ensure that the noise level meets the code requirements.

Add the required decibel gain as required by the code. On the test surface, set the sensitivity by setting the lateral wave amplitude at 40% to 90% (40% and 80% EN) of the full screen height (FSH) and verify the acceptable noise level is not exceeded.

Note: For situations where the lateral wave cannot be used (for example surface conditions, steep

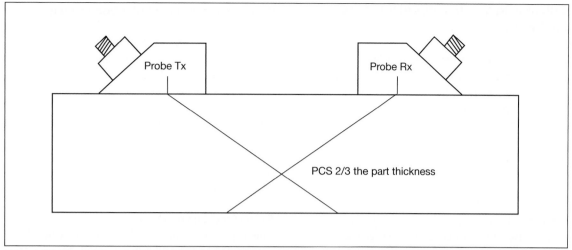

Figure 23: The probe center spacing (PCS) is the point where ultrasonic waves from the two probes would theoretically cross at two-thirds of the depth of the part being inspected.

beam angles), the sensitivity shall be set such that the amplitude of the backwall signal is between 18 dB and 30 dB above FSH. When the use of neither a lateral wave, nor a backwall signal is appropriate, sensitivity should be set such that the material grain noise is between 5% and 10% FSH. Note that a higher frequency has lower amplitude lateral waves.

Calculating Probe Center Spacing

The first step in the setup of a TOFD system is to calculate the probe center spacing (PCS). The PCS is the distance measured between the exit points of the transmitter (Tx) and receiver (Rx) probes.

It's the point where the ultrasonic waves from the two probes used would theoretically cross at two-thirds of the depth of the part being inspected (Figure 23).

Note: The probe exit points can be located by placing the transducer probes together and moving them slightly until the signal peaks. Mark the transducer exit points on the wedge.

In some situations, a correctly calculated PCS can lead to false indications from the weld reinforcement.

An incorrect PCS may lead to incomplete coverage of the weld and heat affected zone. In these cases, the probes may require repositioning or multi-sets of probes may be used.

For a given inspection, Equation 4 is used to calculate PCS.

(Eq. 4) $\quad PCS = 2 \cdot D \cdot \tan \alpha$

where
  2 is constant,
  D is 2/3 material thickness, and
  α is inspection angle.

Calculate the PCS for a one-half (12.7 mm) weld inspection using a single pair of 70° probes.

$$PCS = 2 \cdot 8.467 \text{ mm} \cdot \tan 70°$$
$$PCS = 2 \cdot 8.467 \text{ mm} \cdot 2.74$$
$$PCS = 46.38 \text{ mm}$$

Calculating the Time of Arrival of the Lateral Wave

The next calculation needed is the arrival time of the lateral wave so that the lateral wave can be positioned correctly on the display.

The arrival time of the lateral wave may be calculated using Equation 5:

(Eq. 5) $\quad t_{LW} = 2 \cdot \dfrac{S}{c} + t_0$

where
  t_{LW} is time to lateral wave,
  S is time to lateral wave distance of probe to weld centerline,
  c is sound velocity in the material inspected, and
  t_0 is wedge delay (the time it takes for the sound wave to travel through the wedge).

Calculating the Time of Arrival of the Backwall

The last calculation needed to complete the setup is the arrival time of the backwall — the time needed for the sound to travel from the transmitter (Tx) probe to the backwall and back to the receiver (Rx) probe in microseconds (µs).

Equation 6 is used to calculate the first longitudinal backwall arrival time:

$$\text{(Eq. 6)} \quad t_{BW} = 2\left(\frac{\sqrt{S2 + D^2}}{c} = t_o\right)$$

where
  S is distance of probe to weld centerline,
  c is sound velocity in the material inspected,
  D is material thickness (mm), and
  t_0 is wedge delay (µs).

Depth and Height of a Discontinuity

It is assumed that the ultrasonic energy enters and leaves the specimen at the index points of the probes.

Calculating Depth of a Discontinuity

When the discontinuity is assumed to be mid-way between two probes, the assumed depth of the discontinuity is given by Equation 7:

$$\text{(Eq. 7)} \quad 1/2d = \left[1/4(ct) - S\right]$$

where
  c is sound velocity of the material inspected,
  t is time of flight of the tip-diffraction signal,
  d is depth of the tip of the discontinuity, and
  S is half the distance between the index points of the ultrasonic probes.

Note: The time of flight of the ultrasonic signal inside the ultrasonic probes (wedge delay) shall be subtracted before the calculation of the depth is made. If the probe delay is not subtracted, significant errors in depth will occur in depth calculations.

Depth (d) caused by wedge delay may be calculated from the time of flight differences, between the lateral wave and the diffracted pulse, using Equation 8.

$$\text{(Eq. 8)} \quad 1/2d = 1/2\left[(ct) + 4ctS\right]$$

Calculating the Height of a Discontinuity

Top-Surface Breaking Discontinuities
The height of a top-surface breaking discontinuity may be determined by the distance between the top surface and the depth of the lower-tip diffraction signal.

Bottom-Surface Breaking Discontinuities
The height of a bottom-surface breaking discontinuity may be determined by the difference in depth between the upper-tip diffraction and the bottom surface.

Embedded Discontinuity
The height of an embedded discontinuity may be determined by the difference in depth between the upper-tip and lower-tip diffraction.

Calculating Dead Zones and Spatial Resolution
The lateral wave dead zone, also called the scanning surface dead zone (D_{ds}), can be calculated by lateral wave using Equation 9:

$$\text{(Eq. 9)} \quad 1/2D_{ds} = \left[ct_p/4 + Sct_p\right]$$

Interference between the lateral wave and the discontinuity indication may obscure the indication.

In addition, a backwall dead zone occurs, due to the backwall echo. The depth of the backwall dead zone may be calculated by Equation 10:

$$\text{(Eq. 10)} \quad 1/2D_{dw} = \left[c\left(t_w + t_p\right)/4 - S\right] - W$$

where
  D_{dw} is backwall dead zone
  t_w is time of flight to the backwall echo,
  t_p is wall thickness of the part inspected,
  c is sound velocity of the material inspected, and
  S is half the distance between the index points of the ultrasonic probes.

Both dead zones can be reduced by decreasing the probe PCS or by using probes with shorter pulse duration.

Spatial Resolution

The spatial resolution (R) is a function of depth and can be calculated by Equation 11:

$$\text{(Eq. 11)} \quad 1/2R = \left[\frac{c\left(t_d + t_p\right)}{4 - S}\right] - d$$

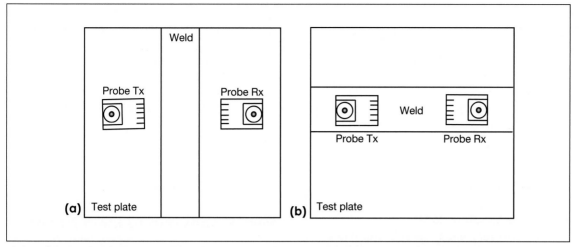

Figure 24: Two basic types of TOFD scans are (a) non-parallel (B-scans) and (b) parallel (longitudinal D-scans).

where

R is spatial resolution,

t_p is duration of the ultrasonic pulse,

t_d is time of flight at depth,

c is sound velocity of the material inspected, and

S is half the distance between the index points of the ultrasonic probes.

Spatial resolution increases with depth, and can be improved by decreasing the probe center separation or the pulse length from the ultrasonic unit.

Scan Types

There are two basic types of TOFD scans. These are parallel (longitudinal D-scans) and non-parallel (B-scans). (See Figure 24.)

When using a parallel scan, the probe motion is parallel to the ultrasonic beam axis.

In non-parallel scans, the probe pair motion is perpendicular to the ultrasonic beam axis.

TOFD probes may also be rastered to ensure complete coverage of certain materials, such as composites, when using TOFD for corrosion monitoring techniques.

Verification Block

TOFD verification blocks may be made using notches and/or side-drilled holes (SDH). The notch ends may be square or pointed.

Single Zone Reference Block (ASME/ASTM)

Once the display has been set up, the sensitivity should be confirmed in accordance with the applicable code and standard. ASTM and ASME require that a verification block (Figure 25) be used.

Dual Zone Inspections (ASME/ASTM)

Multiple probes are used to inspect different zones of thicknesses (depths) in thick parts. These types of scans are sometimes called *dual zone* or *multizone techniques*.

On thick parts, it may not be possible to see both the lateral wave and backwall at the same time. Thick parts require that additional probes with different angles and different PCSs be added to cover the thicker areas and a new reference point be established.

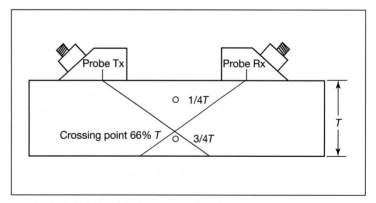

Figure 25: Single zone verification block.

This is done by using an additional side-drilled hole (SDH) inserted into a reference standard. These SDHs can be used to ensure that full coverage of the thicker area(s) of the part is inspected (Figure 26).

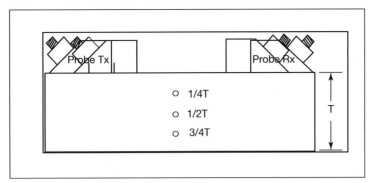

Figure 26: Dual zone verification block.

EN 583 Verification Block

EN 583 verification block uses side-drilled holes with a diameter of at least twice the wavelength of the nominal frequency of the probes.

Saw cuts are made from the scanning surface to the top of the side-drilled holes in the block to enable the direct reflection from the top of the hole (Figure 27).

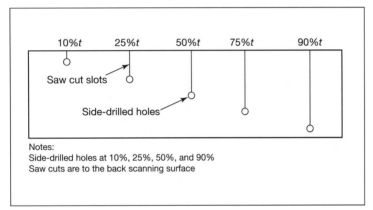

Figure 27: EN 583 verification block.

The maximum diffraction efficiency occurs when the target or discontinuity angle is about 120°.

The probes should be arranged such that the beams' centerlines intersect at about this angle in the region where discontinuities are located. Deviations of more than –35° or +45° from this value may cause the diffracted echoes to be weak.

The reference block thickness should be chosen so that the beam angle at the bottom of the reference block is not smaller than 40°. This avoids having a zone where there is no diffraction at the bottom of the block.

This thickness may be calculated using Equation 12:

$$\text{(Eq. 12)} \qquad T_{max} = (Z \tan \alpha) / \tan 40°$$

where

T_{max} is maximum thickness of the calibration block,

Z is 2/3 thickness of the test block,

α is constant.

$$T_{max} = (23.3 \cdot \tan 60°)/\tan 40° = 48.1 \text{ mm}$$

where

$t = 35$ mm

$\alpha = 60°$

$Z = 2/3\ t\ (23.3\ \text{mm})$

Multi-Probes and Tandem Probes

In most TOFD inspections, we assume that the discontinuity is located directly between the probes. The exact position of the reflector can only be determined by performing at least two scans.

If a more accurate assessment of the position and orientation of the discontinuity is required, multiple scans must be performed. They may be parallel, non-parallel, or both.

Multiple offset probes and tandem probes are used to determine a more precise location of a discontinuity and add additional coverage on thick or oddly shaped specimens (Figures 28 and 29).

If the image of the discontinuity shows up in one scan and not the other, it is located in between that set of probes. If a discontinuity shows up in both sets of probes, the set of probes where the indication is visualized farthest down in time (deepest in the scan) is the one where the discontinuity is closest to the center of that set of probes.

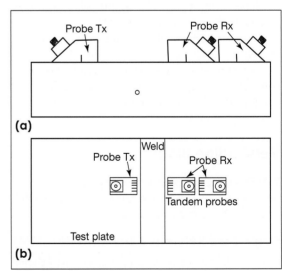

Figure 28: Tandem probe setup: (a) side view; (b) top view.

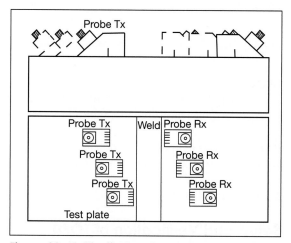

Figure 29: Multi-offset probes setup.

Procedures, Scan Plans, and Their Qualification

Written procedures are required by most codes when performing TOFD inspection.

In addition, written scan plans may also be required for each weld or part inspected.

Scan plans are work instructions for the inspector to use when performing TOFD inspection (Figure 30). Scan plans may be created using conventional ultrasonic calculations: TOFD formulas, spreadsheets, AutoCAD, or other specialized computer software programs.

Remember that the selection of TOFD probes and wedges is based on depth of focus, sensitivity, penetrating power, and coverage of the examination.

TOFD models developed by computer software create sketches as if both probes have beam spread. In actuality, only one probe emits energy — the other receives energy. However, any sound emitted from a source outside the beam spread of the receiving probe will not be picked up by the receiving probe. Therefore, the beam spread of both probes needs to be considered in inspection and inspection modeling.

Some codes and standards require the development of a scan plan prior to inspection.

One problem with TOFD inspections is the failure to identify the area inspected. We should always ask just how much of the weld and heat affected zone (HAZ) are we inspecting.

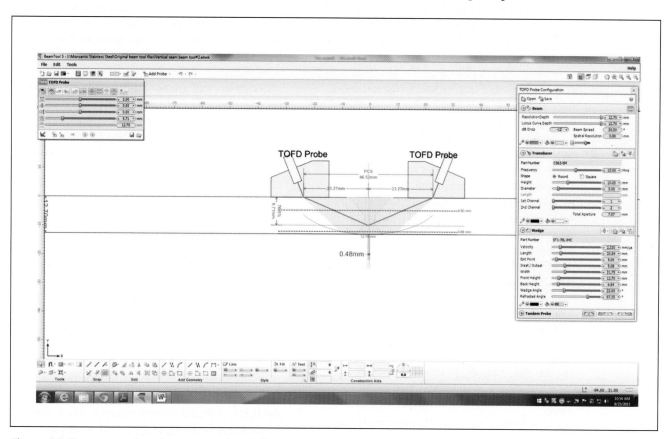

Figure 30: Screen capture from scan plan software.

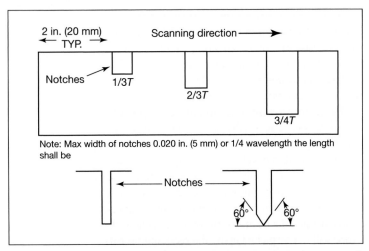

Figure 31: Example of flat ASME demonstration block with three notches.

The HAZ is the area next to the weld affected by welding. For the weld inspection, it is usually 0.5 in. (12.7 mm) to 1 in. (25.4 mm) depending on the code or standard, or is calculated using the EN standard. Another method is to actually measure the HAZ at the time the welding procedure is qualified using a macro etch of the weld.

The complete weld and HAZ must be covered. This may require the use of additional ultrasonic techniques such as phased array, conventional pulse echo, or pitch and catch added to the test procedure and/or the addition of other test methods such as magnetic particle.

Some codes require that the inspection procedure and scan plan be qualified.

Depending on the code or standard, a test coupon should be scanned and the results compared to known discontinues. This may be done with comparison to another NDT method or by measuring the dimension of a discontinuity mechanically. Figure 31 is an example of a TOFD ASME block used when qualification is required by ASME Mandatory Appendix L.

Sizing accuracy (%) may be determined on the length of known discontinuities using Equations 13 and 14:

(Eq. 13) $\left(D_d - D_m / D_m\right) \times 100 = \%$ accuracy in depth

where

D_d is depth as measured by the TOFD system, and

D_m is depth as measured mechanically.

(Eq. 14) $\left(L_d - L_m / L_m\right) 100 = \%$ accuracy in length

where

L_d is length as measured by TOFD system, and

L_m is length as measured mechanically.

Remember, it is not possible to obtain 100% coverage of most welds using only TOFD. One of the major purposes of a scan plan is to identify the areas that are missed.

Setup and Verification of TOFD System

Scanning and Encoding

TOFD scans are normally single axis, one-line scans, focused at two-thirds (66%) of the weld thickness or part thickness.

Calibrating the Encoder

It is important to calibrate the encoder for accuracy prior to use. It is also important to check the encoder for accuracy after the inspection is completed or during the inspection if a malfunction is suspected.

Encoders that are not calibrated or malfunctioning, may lead to the improper positioning of the discontinuity in the scan axis.

Encoder calibrations and checks should be carried out in accordance with the reference codes. Loss of data (skips) may also occur when the scanning speed is too high or the encoder is damaged or broken.

Calibrating TOFD

TOFD is one of the few NDT methods that are calibrated after the inspection data is collected.

Typically the TOFD image may be calibrated by one or two common methods:
- calibrate the display using the lateral wave and backwall echo, or
- calibrate the display using the velocity of the material and the velocity of the wedge.

When calibrating the display, the inspector can use either of the following positions in the A-scan:
- calibrate the first half-cycle peak in the RF display, or
- calibrate at the crossover between the first and second half-cycle peak in the RF display.

Measurements used for calibration should always be taken from the same point of reference. Calibration using the backwall should not be used when the material thickness is uncertain, when the wall thickness varies, or during inservice inspections.

Evaluating a Scan

Assessing the Quality of the TOFD Image

Prior to the evaluation of a TOFD inspection, the quality of the TOFD image should be assessed.
Causes of poor quality images:
- Gain setting too low — amplitude of lateral wave < 40% FSH.
- Gain setting too high — amplitude of lateral wave > 80% FSH (saturated).
- Inappropriate time window setting — lateral wave is not present in the time window.
- Image influenced by variation of couplant thickness (may be straightened by software).
- Missing scan lines caused by high scanning speeds.
- Time-base triggering problems.
- Electrical interference.
- Relevant indications.

Evaluation of TOFD Scans

Once the acceptability of the scan has been evaluated, the inspector must evaluate the part as to its acceptability. The inspector must determine if the indications are relevant or nonrelevant.

TOFD indications are identified by patterns or disturbances in the image. TOFD provides an image of the discontinuities in the weld as well as the geometric features of the test specimen. TOFD indication patterns include:
- Disturbance of the lateral wave.
- Disturbance of the backwall reflection.
- Indications between the lateral wave and backwall reflection.
- Phase of indications between the lateral wave and backwall reflection.
- Mode converted signals after the first backwall reflection.

In order to identify indications of geometry, knowledge of the test object is required. Indications originating from the geometry of the part, the corner of a counter sink for example, are considered nonrelevant.

To decide whether an indication is relevant (caused by a discontinuity), patterns or disturbances have to be evaluated considering shape and signal amplitude relative to general noise level.

To determine the extent of an indication, you may need to take into account gray level values and/or patterns of neighboring sections.

Relevant Indications

Relevant indications can be classified as those that are surface-breaking to embedded. Amplitude, phase, location, and patterns of relevant indications may contain information on the type of discontinuity.

Measuring Discontinuities

The size of a discontinuity is determined by its length and height. Length is defined by the difference of the scan axis at the extremities of the indication. The height is defined as the maximum difference of thinness and the thickness of the part. For indications displaying varying coordinates in the scan axis along their length, the height should be determined at the thickness where the difference of the scan axis is greatest (Figure 32).

Before starting to evaluate indications, inspectors should look at some important factors that will help in the evaluation.

TOFD Evaluation Tips

TOFD scans are easily affected by the surface conditions of the test specimen. Surface roughness, as little as 0.02 in. (0.5 mm), may cause a loss of the lateral wave. A loss of the lateral wave is a loss of signal, and no discontinuities can be located in this area of the inspection.

Improper adjustment of the wedge wear plates and/or rough surfaces may cause nonrelevant indications at the lateral wave; it will appear as an OD connected indication right below the lateral wave.

The diffracted top tip of a crack appears weaker than the bottom by about 4 dB, depending upon the amplitude of the crack.

The diffracted top tip of a planar discontinuity (slag, incomplete penetration) appears stronger than that of the bottom tip.

There may be no loss of backwall for root indications, such as incomplete penetration or burn through.

The inspector should include the shear wave backwall reflection in the scans. Some discontinuities may be revealed in the more sensitive refracted shear wave than those viewed in the longitudinal wave. Indications in the shear wave that are not detected in the longitudinal beam are most likely located under the transducer.

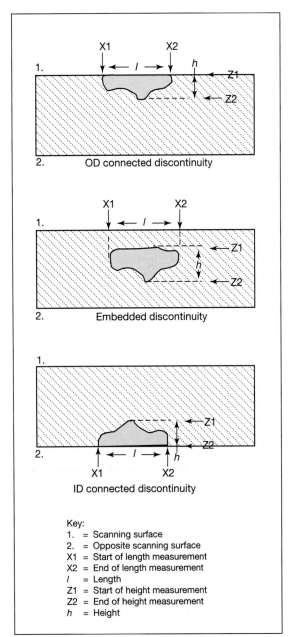

Key:
1. = Scanning surface
2. = Opposite scanning surface
X1 = Start of length measurement
X2 = End of length measurement
l = Length
Z1 = Start of height measurement
Z2 = End of height measurement
h = Height

Figure 32: Method of measuring indications.

Adding Software Gain (Contrast) During Evaluation

Soft gain, sometimes called software gain, can be added after the data is collected in some systems. Soft gain is used to enhance weak responses typical of cracks. It is also used to enhance contrast when measuring discontinuity lengths.

Signals over 100% FSH cannot be adjusted by software gain, in addition, increasing gain over 12 dB should be avoided.

TOFD Codes and Standards

The current codes and standards regarding TOFD inspections consist of both American and European standards.

American Standards

- *ASME Boiler and Pressure Vessel Code*, Section V, Non-Mandatory Appendix L, TOFD sizing demonstration/Dual Probe — Computer Imaging Technique TOFD.
- *ASME Boiler and Pressure Vessel Code*, Section V, Article 4, Appendix III, Time of Flight Diffraction Technique.
- *ASTM E 2373-09*: Standard Practice for the Use of the Ultrasonic Time of Flight Diffraction (TOFD) Technique.

EN Standards

- *EN 583-6 Nondestructive Testing, Ultrasonic Examinations* — Part 6: Time of Flight Diffraction Technique as a Method of Detection and Sizing Discontinuities.
- *EN 15617 Nondestructive Testing of Welds* — Time of Flight Diffraction Technique (TOFD) — Acceptance Levels.
- *EN ISO 10863 Welding.* Use of Time of Flight Diffraction Technique (TOFD) for Examination of Welds. This document specifies four examination levels (A, B, C, D) corresponding to an increasing level of inspection reliability. Guidance on the selection of examination levels is also provided in this document.

Reference Blocks and Written Procedure

Codes and standards have varying requirements for the type of reference blocks to be used to verify the sensitivity and coverage of a TOFD inspection.

To comply with ASME Section V, Article 4 and the requirements of Appendix III, reference blocks are required and a written procedure must be developed.

EN ISO 10863 has four levels of examinations. When working to Levels A and B, verification blocks are required for setup. Sensitivity reference blocks are required for levels B, C, and D. A written procedure must be developed for examination levels C and D. The standard itself (no procedure development required) may be used for examination levels A and B.

The identification, sizing, and verification of the setup varies among the codes and standards. The TOFD inspector must be familiar with the requirements of each code and standard and be familiar with any procedures and scan plans developed for the inspection.

Identification of discontinuities per EN ISO 10863:

- Scanning surface discontinuity — This type shows up as an elongated pattern generated by the signal emitted from the lower edge of the discontinuity and a weakening or loss of the lateral wave (not always observed). The indication from the lower edge can be hidden by the lateral wave, but generally a pattern can be observed in the mode-converted part of the image. For small discontinuities, only a small delay of the lateral wave may be observed.
- Opposite surface discontinuity — This type shows up as an elongated pattern generated by the signal emitted from the upper edge of the discontinuity and a weakening, loss, or delay of the backwall reflection (not always observed).
- Through-wall discontinuity — This type shows up as a loss or weakening of both the lateral wave and the backwall reflection accompanied by diffracted signals from both ends of the discontinuity.
- Point-like discontinuity — This type shows up as a single hyperbolic shaped curve, which may lie at any depth.
- Elongated discontinuities with no measurable height — This type appears as an elongated pattern corresponding to an apparent upper edge signal.
- Elongated discontinuity with measurable height — This type appears as two elongated patterns, located at different positions in depth, corresponding to the lower and upper edges of the discontinuity. The indication of the lower edge is usually in phase with the lateral wave. The indication of the upper edge is usually in phase with the backwall reflection. Indications of embedded discontinuities usually do not disturb the lateral wave or the backwall reflection.

Identification of discontinuities per ASME Section V, Article 4, Appendix L:

- Top-surface connected flaws — Flaw indications consisting solely of a lower-tip diffracted signal and with an associated weakening, shift, or interruption of the lateral wave signal, shall be considered as extending to the top surface unless further evaluated by other NDE methods.
- Embedded flaws — Flaw indications with both an upper- and lower-tip diffracted signal or solely an upper-tip diffracted signal with no associated weakening, shift, or interruption of

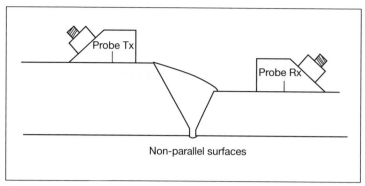

Figure 33: Corrections in calculating offset surfaces.

Non-parallel surfaces

the backwall signal shall be considered embedded.
- Bottom-surface connected flaws — Flaw indications consisting solely of an upper-tip diffracted signal and an associated shift of the backwall or interruption of the backwall signal, shall be considered as extending to the bottom surface unless further evaluated by other NDE methods.

Flaw height determination per ASME Section V:

- Top-surface connected flaws — The height of a top-surface connected flaw shall be determined by the distance between the top-surface lateral wave and the lower-tip diffracted signal.
- Embedded flaws — The height (h) of an embedded flaw shall be determined by the distance between the upper-tip diffracted signal and the lower-tip diffracted signal. For discontinuities with just a singular upper-tip diffracted signal, use Equation 15.

(Eq. 15) $$hp = \left\{ \left[c(td + tp)/2 \right]^2 - S^2 \right\}^{1/2} - d$$

where

d is depth,
t is time from transmitter to receiver,
t_0 is wedge delay,
c is velocity,
S is 1/2 PCS.

Complex Geometry

The principles for flat plate are also used for testing other geometries; however, the sizing and interpretation of results may be more complex than for flat plate. For examination other than flat plate, detection and coverage must be qualified.

Phase inversion considerations may be part of the evaluation technique and assessed for sizing and depth estimates.

Offset Scanning Surfaces

In order to calculate the depth when inspecting plates with different wall thicknesses (Figure 33), Equation 16 is required to correct the depth and height location of any discontinuities detected.

$$\text{(Eq. 16)} \qquad \delta d = \frac{H}{2} \times \left(1 + \frac{d^2}{2S^2}\right)$$

δd is depth of reflector in a non-parallel surface examination,
d is depth of reflector from thinner of the two scan surfaces,
H is offset or difference in wall thickness between the two materials,
S is 1/2 PCS.

Concave Surfaces

Scanning from a concave surface introduces the concept of the lateral wave as a creeping wave. This applies to the condition where the refracted beam is in compression mode.

Scanning from a Convex Surface

These configurations introduce the lateral wave as a combined compression and creeping wave.

TOFD Inspection of Nozzles and Other Complex Shapes

Nozzles and T, K, and Y connections may be inspected using TOFD; however, they require advanced TOFD modeling software.

In addition, mock-ups are necessary to ensure that the modeling is correct. The evaluation of these scans may include multiple backwall and evaluation of the shear components.

Summary

Simple TOFD inspections are easy to set-up and perform, and are extremely accurate for sizing. TOFD inspections can be performed at high speeds and at elevated temperatures with results that are easy to evaluate.

We also have learned TOFD inspections due to dead zones caused by loci at the near and far surfaces of the test part and the lack of resolution at the far surface TOFD may not be relied on as the only inspection method when 100% of a weld or part is to be inspected. In addition, the lack of detection at contact angles close to 38° may cause some discontinuites to be missed during TOFD inspections.

Complex geometry requires a much greater knowledge of TOFD principles and advanced modeling software.

Review Questions

1. When developing TOFD ultrasonic inspection techniques, which of the following wave forms are most likely to be used to inspect a 1 in. (25 mm) carbon steel weld?

   a. Shear.
   b. Longitudinal.
   c. Plate.
   d. Lamb.

2. Indications viewed in the TOFD display are detected by which of the following?

   a. Reflected waves.
   b. Surface waves.
   c. Creeping waves.
   d. Diffracted waves.

3. Of the following probe setups, which are used for TOFD inspections?

   a. Pitch and catch.
   b. Pulse echo.
   c. Through-transmission.
   d. Dual beam.

4. Which of the following is an advantage of a TOFD ultrasonic inspection?

   a. Optimum probe center spacing (PCS) may result in probe interference with weld cap.
   b. Less sensitive to discontinuity orientation.
   c. Requires an additional scan to approximate which side of the weld the discontinuity is located.
   d. Mismatch (high low) conditions may mask root discontinuities in backwall signal.

5. The TOFD image is made up of which of the following?

   a. Stacked B-scans.
   b. Stacked A-scans.
   c. Stacked C-scans.
   d. Stacked grayscale images.

6. The wave traveling between the probes at the test surface is called the:

   a. lateral wave.
   b. backwall.
   c. second backwall.
   d. discontinuity.

7. In the RF A-scan display without a discontinuity (Figure 34), which signal is the lateral wave?

   a. 1
   b. 2
   c. 3
   d. 4

8. In the RF A-scan display without a discontinuity (Figure 34), which signal is the longitudinal backwall?

   a. 1
   b. 2
   c. 3
   d. 4

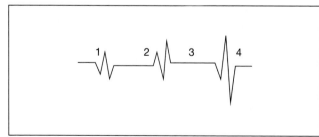

Figure 34

9. In the RF A-scan display with a fully embedded discontinuity (Figure 35), which signal is the longitudinal backwall?

    a. 2
    b. 3
    c. 4
    d. 5

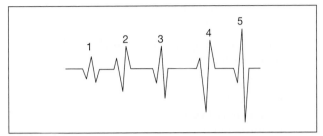

Figure 35

10. In the RF A-scan display with a fully embedded discontinuity (Figure 35), which signal is the bottom tip of the discontinuity?

    a. 2
    b. 3
    c. 4
    d. 5

11. In the A-scan in Figure 36, what type of discontinuity is displayed?

    a. OD connected.
    b. ID connected.
    c. Fully embedded.
    d. No discontinuity detected.

12. In the RF A-scan (Figure 36), which signal is the lateral wave?

    a. 1
    b. 2
    c. 3
    d. 4

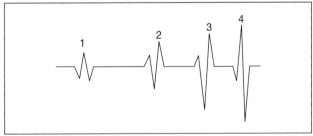

Figure 36

13. Frequencies used for TOFD inspection are most dependent on:

    a. the thickness of the thinner part.
    b. near field, beam spread, and the reflection factor of the material.
    c. acoustic impedance, beam spread, and penetrating ability.
    d. sensitivity, beam spread, and penetrating ability.

14. When performing TOFD inspections of some stainless steels, frequencies as low as _____ may be required.

    a. 10 MHz
    b. 5 MHz
    c. 2 MHz
    d. 20 MHz

15. Good TOFD probes have:

    a. high damping.
    b. low damping.
    c. damping has little effect on TOFD probes.
    d. TOFD probes require no damping.

16. The most common test frequencies used for TOFD inspections range between:

    a. 2 MHz and 10 MHz.
    b. 5 MHz and 15 MHz.
    c. 2 MHz and 10 MHz.
    d. 5 KHz and 10 MHz.

17. The type of view most commonly used to evaluate TOFD inspections is:

    a. A-scan.
    b. B-scan.
    c. C-scan.
    d. D-scan.

18. The type of view most commonly used to set and calibrate TOFD inspections is:

    a. A-scan.
    b. D-scan.
    c. C-scan.
    d. RF A-scan.

19. Normal probe sizes for TOFD inspections are:

    a. 1/16 in. to 1/8 in. (1.6 mm to 3.2 mm).
    b. 1/8 in. to 1/4 in. (3.2 mm to 6.4 mm).
    c. 1/4 in. to 3/8 in. (6.4 mm to 9.5 mm).
    d. 1/2 in. to 3/4 in. (12.7 mm to 19 mm).

20. The maximum ring time for a TOFD inspection should be no more than:

   a. 1 cycle.
   b. 2 cycles.
   c. 3 cycles.
   d. 4 cycles.

21. Because indications turn down at their ends, which of the following is the most common measurement tool used in TOFD inspections?

   a. Hyperbolic cursors.
   b. SAFT cursors.
   c. Removal of the backwall.
   d. Straightening of the backwall.

22. Removal of the lateral wave improves resolution for:

   a. indications located in or near the lateral wave.
   b. all indications.
   c. indications in the lateral wave not connected to the OD.
   d. indications connected to the ID.

23. Incorrect positioning of the lateral wave may cause:

   a. incorrect depth of indication.
   b. incorrect surface distance to the discontinuity.
   c. incorrect measurement of the discontinuity length.
   d. a lack of coverage of the weld and heat affected zone.

24. Which of the following best describes the probe center spacing (PCS)?

   a. Spacing from the front of the probes where the sound beams of two transducers cross at two-thirds the weld thickness.
   b. Spacing measured from the index position on the wedge where two transducers cross two-thirds of the weld thickness.
   c. Spacing from the back of the wedge where the probes cross at one-half of the weld thickness.
   d. Spacing from the front of the wedge where the probe spacing crosses at three-fourths the weld thickness.

25. A TOFD inspector inspecting a 0.50 in. (12.7 mm) thick single V groove weld uses a set of 70° longitudinal wedges. The crossing point of the weld is two-thirds of the depth. Which of the following is the correct PCS for this inspection?

   a. 1.667 in. (42.34 mm)
   b. 1832 in. (47 295 mm)
   c. 1.832 in. (47.3 mm)
   d. 1667 in. (42 342 mm)

26. In this grayscale image without a discontinuity (Figure 37), which of the following is the lateral wave?

   a. 1
   b. 2
   c. 3
   d. 4

27. In the grayscale image without a discontinuity above (Figure 37), which of the following is the shear wave component?

   a. 1
   b. 2
   c. 3
   d. 4

28. In the grayscale image without a discontinuity above (Figure 37), which of the following is the shear wave backwall?

   a. 2
   b. 3
   c. 4
   d. 5

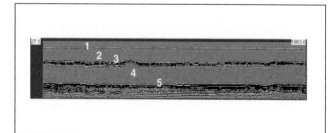

Figure 37

Answers

1b	2d	3a	4b	5b	6a	7a	8b	9d	10b	11b	12a	13d
14c	15a	16b	17b	18d	19c	20b	21a	22a	23d	24b	25c	26a
27d	28d											

CHAPTER 6
Phased Array

Introduction

History of Phased Array

Industrial phased array ultrasonic technology (PAUT) has evolved from similar phased array technology used in radar, sonar, and medical imaging. As phased array technology advanced, higher frequency, shorter wavelength signals were evaluated. (Medical phased arrays were developed for detecting cancers, imaging internal organs, and measuring blood flow rates.) Despite the fact that the physics of phased array ultrasonics are identical, there are many significant differences between medical and industrial applications. Medical ultrasound uses longitudinal wave mode propagation, whereas industrial ultrasonics can use either longitudinal or shear wave modes. More significantly, medical scans typically try to image small reflectivity differences between soft tissues, which requires a considerable amount of resolution. In addition, the medical ultrasonographer scans human bodies, which are generally of similar composition, whereas industrial arrays may inspect components of different thicknesses, geometries, materials, and discontinuities. Overall, medical and industrial phased arrays are two dissimilar applications.

Basic Principles of Phased Array

Concepts and Theory

Ultrasonic phased array is a novel method of generating and receiving ultrasound. It uses multiple ultrasonic elements and electronic time delays to create sound beams by constructive and destructive interference. As such, phased arrays offer significant technical advantages over conventional single-element or dual-element ultrasonics; the phased array beams can be steered, scanned, swept, and focused electronically (Figure 1).

- Electronic scanning permits very rapid coverage of components being inspected; typically an order of magnitude faster than a single probe mechanical system.
- Sound beam forming permits the selected beam angles to be ultrasonically optimized by orienting them perpendicular to the predicted discontinuities.
- Sound beam steering (also called sectorial scanning) can be used for mapping components at appropriate angles to optimize probability of detection. Sectorial scanning is useful for inspections where the probe-scanning surface is limited.

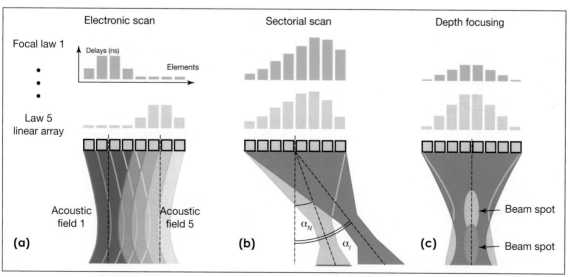

Figure 1: Generation of linear and sectorial scans using phased arrays: (a) linear focusing; (b) sectorial focusing; (c) depth focusing.

- Electronic focusing permits optimizing the sound beam shape and size at the expected discontinuities location, as well as optimizing probability of detection. Focusing improves the signal-to-noise ratio significantly, which also permits operating at lower pulser voltage and receiver gain, or using less amplification gain.

Overall, the use of phased arrays permits optimizing discontinuities detection while minimizing inspection time.

How Phased Arrays Work

Phased arrays use an array of acoustic elements, all individually wired, pulsed, and time-shifted. These elements can form a linear array, a 2D matrix array, a circular array, or other more complex forms. Most applications use linear arrays since these are the easiest to program and are significantly cheaper than more complex arrays.

Each element is acoustically and electrically isolated from one another and packaged in a single-probe housing. The cables connecting the probe to the instrument usually consist of a bundle of well-shielded micro-coaxial cables with a commercial multichannel connector that connects it to a phased array instrument.

Elements are typically pulsed in groups of 4 to 32; typically 16 elements are used for weld inspection. With a user-friendly system, the computer and software calculate the time delays for a setup from operator-input on inspection angle, focal distance, and scan pattern, or use a predefined file. The time delays are back calculated using time of flight from the focal spot, and the scan assembled from individual focal laws. Time delay circuits must be accurate to around 2 ns to provide the phasing accuracy required.

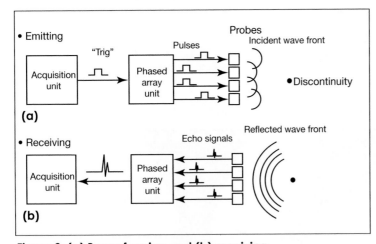

Figure 2: (a) Beam forming and (b) receiving.

Each element generates a beam when pulsed; these beams constructively and destructively interfere to form a wave front. (This interference can be seen, for example, with photo-elastic imaging — Ginzel, 2004*). The phased array instrumentation pulses the individual channels with time delays as specified to form a precalculated wave front. For receiving, the instrumentation effectively performs the reverse — it receives with precalculated time delays, then sums the time-shifted signal and displays it (Figure 2).

The summed waveform is effectively identical to a single channel flaw detector using a probe with the same angle, frequency, focusing, and aperture. Sample scan patterns are shown in Figure 3.

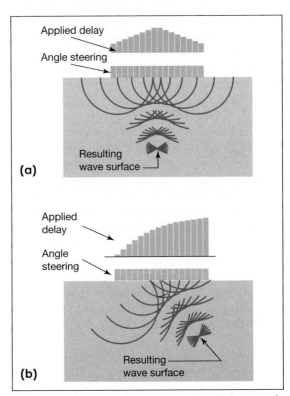

Figure 3: Schematic time delays (top histograms) for (a) focused normal beam and (b) focused shear wave.

Practical Application of Phased Arrays

From a practical viewpoint, ultrasonic phased array is merely a method of generating and receiving ultrasound; once the ultrasound is in the material, it is independent of the generation method, whether generated by piezoelectric, electromagnetic, laser, or phased arrays. Consequently, many of

---

*All references for this chapter are listed on page v.

the details of ultrasonic inspection remain unchanged; for example, if 5 MHz is the optimum inspection frequency with conventional ultrasonics, then phased arrays would typically start by using the same frequency, aperture size, focal length, and incident angle.

While phased arrays require well-developed instrumentation, one of the key requirements is good, user-friendly software. Besides calculating the focal laws, the software saves and displays the results, and the ability to manipulate data is essential. As phased arrays offer considerable application flexibility, software versatility is highly desirable. Phased array inspections can be manual, semiautomated (encoded), or fully automated, depending on the application, speed, and budget. Encoder capability and full data storage are usually required.

Though it can be time consuming to prepare the first setup, the information is recorded and takes only seconds to reload. Also, modifying a prepared setup is quick in comparison with physically adjusting conventional probes.

Typical Applications

Realistically, there is no typical application for phased arrays; phased arrays are very flexible and can address many types of inspection problems. Consequently, ultrasonic phased arrays are used in a wide variety of industries where the technology has inherent advantages. These industries include aerospace, nuclear power, steel mills, pipe mills, petrochemical plants, pipeline construction, general manufacturing, and construction, plus a selection of special applications. All these applications take advantage of one or more of the dominant features of phased arrays:

- **Speed**: scanning with phased arrays is much faster than conventional single probe mechanical systems, with better coverage.
- **Flexibility**: setups can be changed in a few minutes, and typically a lot more component dimensional flexibility is available.
- **Inspection angles**: a wide variety of inspection angles can be used, depending on the requirements and the array.
- **Small footprint**: small matrix arrays can give significantly more flexibility for inspecting restricted areas than conventional probes.
- **Imaging**: showing a true depth image of discontinuities is much easier to interpret than a conventional A-scan. The data can be saved and redisplayed as required.

Equipment

Computer-Based Systems

All phased array systems are computer based or digital. For some systems, the computer may be built into the instrument; in other cases (mostly larger and more expensive systems), the computer is a separate system component.

Processors

The processor has a number of functions to perform: adjust the time delays, collect the data, digitize the data using an A/D converter, display the data — and ultimately to analyze the data with the operator's assistance.

Multi-Element/Multichannel Configurations

Predictably, some phased array instruments are required to perform more than a simple one axis scan. For some portable units, limited combinations of probes and connections are possible. Other instruments have multiple connections. This can be overcome by using splitter cables so that combinations can be programmed for advanced applications.

Portable Battery-Operated versus Full Computer-Based Systems

The instrument may limit the types of applications that can be addressed. Portable phased array units are very flexible, but limited in their overall capability regarding speed, functions, number of channels, and so on. The full, dedicated computer-based systems, such as for pipe mills or pipelines, tend to have much higher speeds, more channels, and are used for specific applications. These large dedicated computerized systems also tend to be more expensive compared to portable systems.

Focal Law Generation

Focal laws (or delay laws) are generated by computer programs that calculate the relative time delays between the various pulsing elements in the array. The focal law calculator takes into account the pitch of the elements, the gaps between the elements, plus all the wedge and material parameters. The wedge parameters include height of the first element, angle of the wedge, and the offset. The array parameters include frequency and wavelength, the total number of elements in the array, the active aperture, and passive aperture (unless a 2D or more complex array is used). In addition, the velocities in the wedge and in the material are required. Also, the focal law calculator takes into consideration the desired focusing (focal point) and the number of elements to create the virtual aperture (focal law).

Onboard Focal Law Generator

These typically have less capability, mainly for cost and efficiency reasons. They are used mainly in portable instruments.

External Focal Law Generator

External focal law calculators are used for more advanced calculations, such as for 2D arrays and complex geometries, among others. External focal law calculators can also be used from modelling programs, which can download the relevant data. The focal law calculator then sends the appropriate information to a focal law generator, which is installed on the phased array instrument. (The focal law calculator is software, which generates the focal law file.) The focal law generator then uses the focal law file to generate the time delays needed for generating phased array beams. Focal law files are generally quite simple, for example an ASCII file containing element number, time delay, and voltages for both transmitters and receivers. These files can be subsequently edited to optimize. The focal law files are usually quite small and can be e-mailed.

Probes

Piezocomposite Materials

Most arrays are made from piezocomposite materials. These materials are a combination of a ceramic piezoelectric material and a polymer binder. The array elements are small and typically have low capacitance and high impedance. Composite ceramic yields electromechanical efficiencies above 60% while solid ceramic is below 50%. Phased array probe construction is similar to conventional single-element probe construction: the probe contains the elements, a matching layer to transfer ultrasound into the component, and damping material to optimize the pulse, housing, and coaxial cables.

Overall, piezocomposite arrays offer better signal-to-noise ratios than traditional piezoceramic probes. This is due to variable apertures for specific focusing applications, highly damped piezocomposite arrays, and frequency improvements, as well as controlled focusing.

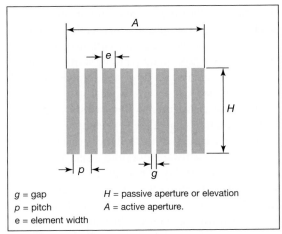

g = gap H = passive aperture or elevation
p = pitch A = active aperture.
e = element width

Figure 4: Schematic of array. This figure applies to 1D arrays only $p = e + g$.

Pitch, Gap, and Size

Pitch, gap, and element size are best defined in Figure 4. The total active probe length (A) can be estimated by:

(Eq. 1) $A = n \times p$

where
   n is the number of elements used by the focal law, and
   p is pitch.

To calculate more precisely the active aperture, use the following equation:

(Eq. 2) $A = (n-1) \times (p+e)$

Passive Aperture or Elevation

The passive aperture plane is one where electronic focusing is not possible, such as the H dimension in Figure 4. Alternative focusing techniques, such as curved arrays, are possible.

Active Aperture

The active aperture plane can be electronically focused in the A direction in Figure 4. Note that the active aperture can be varied by firing a different number of elements. In addition, 2D arrays can typically perform focusing in the direction of both X and Y axes.

Array Configurations

One-dimensional or linear array probes are made using a set of elements juxtaposed and aligned along a linear axis. They enable a beam to be rastered, focused, swept, and steered along a single azimuthal plane (active axis) only. They are very common and are probably used for 90% of the applications.

Two-dimensional or matrix array probes have an active area divided in two dimensions using different elements. Matrix array probes are typically in a checkerboard format, though other designs are used. These probes allow ultrasonic beam steering, and other techniques, in multiple planes.

Sparse matrix arrays contain less than 100% coverage with elements such that gaps occur between elements. Sparse arrays are typically used in larger arrays where instrumentation and array costs are significant.

Annular array probes have the transducers configured as a set of concentric rings that allow the beam to be focused to different depths along an axis. The surface area of each annulus is typically designed to be the same from element to element, in one array probe. This implies that each annulus has a different width.

Sectorial array probes are annular array probes with the annular rings subdivided into multiple elements.

Circular array probes have elements positioned on a cylindrical form. Circular arrays are typically used for tube inspection from the inside diameter without having to use a reflecting mirror.

Daisy array probes have circular elements shaped like slices of a pie curved into a circle so that the ultrasound is emitted along the axis of the circle/cylinder. This type of array can be used with a mirror to inspect from the inside of tubes.

Convex array probes are designed for the inspection of materials with convex curvature.

Concave array probes are designed for inspection of cylindrical product forms from the outside diameter.

Beam and Wave-Forming

Acoustic beam-forming occurs during the transmit cycle of the phased array inspection. It produces the ultrasonic wave that propagates in the material being inspected. Individual piezoelectric array elements are pulsed in sequence according to the delay law specified by the instrumentation. Each element produces its characteristic acoustic wave that propagates and interacts with the waves from adjacent elements, and wave forming is an integral part of phased arrays.

Wave forming occurs during the receive cycle of the phased array inspection. As shown in Figure 5, the acoustic wave from a reflector is received at each array element. The arrival time at each element is different depending on the element's location compared to the source of the reflection. Each individual receive channel applies the inverse delay law to reconstruct the RF waveform from the individual signals received at each array element.

Grating Lobes

Grating lobes are similar to side lobes, but are exclusive to phased arrays. Essentially, the regular structure of arrays creates defined signals at specific angles, depending on the array frequency and element spacing. Figure 6 shows an example of modeled results with a 33-element array

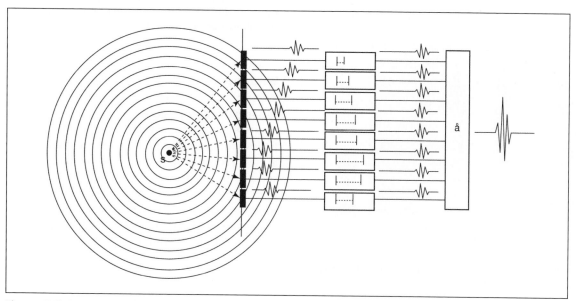

Figure 5: Schematic of beam forming.

(Figure 6a), and a nine-element sparse array (Figure 6b). The nine-element array has similar beam strength of the main signal, but shows much higher noise levels away from the main signal. Note the two grating lobes in Figure 6b. (All other parameters are equal: element size, array width, focusing.)

Grating lobes can be analyzed using a fast fourier transform (FFT). Here, the influence of element pitch becomes clear: as pitch goes down, the grating lobe distance and amplitude decrease, as shown in Figure 7. Effectively, array lobes reduce useful steering range and may generate multiple images.

In practice, array lobes rarely occur as they are essentially designed out. The equation is straightforward:

(Eq. 3) $$\theta_{lobe} = \pm \frac{\lambda}{p}$$

where

θ_{lobe} is the predicted angle for grating lobes, and λ and p have their usual meaning.

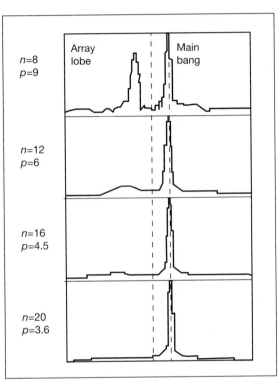

Figure 7: Modeled data showing influence of pitch and number of elements on location and amplitude of grating lobes.

Wedges

Types of Wedge Designs

Figure 8 shows sample wedge designs. Wedges typically are designed for coupling as well as angles, frequency, and more. The manufacturer specifies the range over which the wedge can perform S-scans without any mechanical interference from the edges of the wedge. In addition, the wedges are designed to minimize any extraneous reflections from the ends.

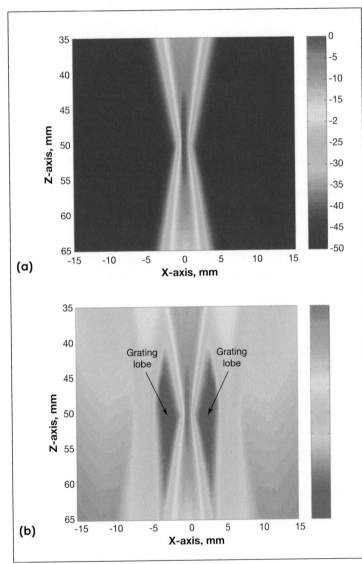

Figure 6: Modeled results showing grating lobes: (a) full array; (b) sparse array with grating lobes arrowed.

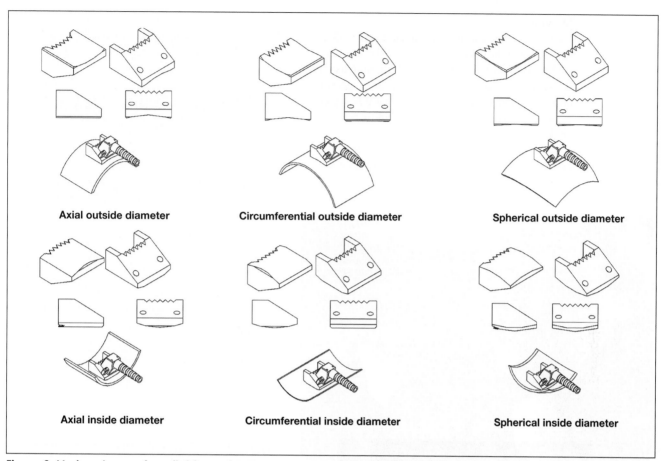

Axial outside diameter

Circumferential outside diameter

Spherical outside diameter

Axial inside diameter

Circumferential inside diameter

Spherical inside diameter

Figure 8: Various types of available wedges.

Scanners

Automated versus Manual Inspections

There are two distinct ways to inspect with phased arrays: automated versus manual. The main differences are the procedures and whether data is collected or not (Davis and Moles).

Mechanized (Automated)

Automated scanners use a motor to drive the delivery system around objects such as pipes and welds, and are usually dedicated to the application in some form. Figure 9 shows an example of an automated scanner in operation. Automated scanners can inspect at high scanning speeds, but are more expensive and complex to operate than manual scanners. There are many approaches, such as magnetic strip followers, welding bands, and robotics, as well as laser tracking.

Figure 9: Automated scanner in action.

In addition, data is collected for analysis and archiving. However, scan plans are required to show coverage and appropriate angles. Overall, these AUT systems are more expensive, but cost effective in appropriate applications.

Manual

Unlike automated scanners, manual scanners do not have motors; the operator must drive the scanner (Figure 10). Consequently, manual scanning tends to be slower than automated scanning, but is cheaper and less complex. The advantage is that it is somewhat faster than conventional UT as more than one angle can be used at the same time.

Note that ASME doesn't accept encoded probes as scanners as these tend to generate results that cannot be reproduced.

Figure 10: Handscanner in action on large-diameter pipe.

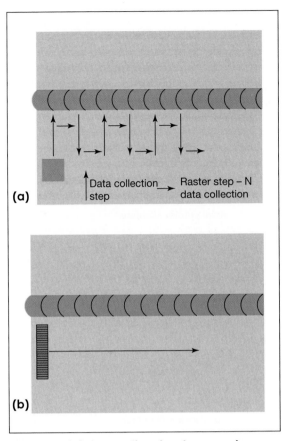

(a)

Data collection step

Raster step – N data collection

(b)

Figure 11: (a) Conventional raster scanning; (b) linear scanning.

Testing Techniques

Electronic pulsing and receiving provide significant opportunities for a variety of scan patterns: electronic scans, sectorial scans (S-scans), linear scans, and combined scans.

Linear Scans

Linear scans, also called one-line scans in the nuclear industry, are single axis scans around a weld or similar component. (See Figure 11b.) Manual ultrasonic weld inspections with conventional probes are performed using a single probe, which the operator scans back and forth in a raster pattern to cover the weld area. Many automated weld inspection systems use a similar approach (Figure 11a), with a conventional single probe scanned back and forth over the weld area. This process is time consuming because of the mechanical motion that needs to occur. Using phased array probes allows simple linear scans without the need to raster scan, saving inspection time. The simplest approach to linear scanning is found in

pipe mills, where a limited number of probes inspect electric resistance welding (ERW) pipe welds (Dubé, 2000). Linear scans are encoded so all data is collected, saved, and displayed. For thicker components, multiple linear scans are used (Figure 12).

Phased arrays offer considerably greater flexibility than conventional automated ultrasonic testing. Typically, it is much easier to change the setup

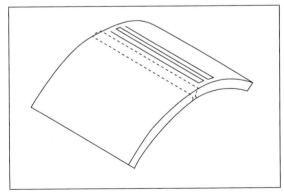

Figure 12: A sample scan pattern on a section of pipe.

electronically, either by modifying the setup or reloading another. Often it is possible to use many more beams (equivalent to individual conventional probes) with phased arrays; special inspections can be implemented simply by loading a setup file.

Sectorial Scans

Sectorial scans are unique to phased arrays. They use the same set of elements, but alter the time delays to sweep the beam through a series of angles (Figure 13). Applications for sectorial scanning typically involve a stationary array, sweeping across a relatively inaccessible component, such as a turbine blade root (Ciorau, et al., 2000), to map out the features and discontinuities. Depending primarily on the array frequency and element spacing, the sweep angles can vary from +20° to +80°. S-scan may also refer to the data display. As a data display, it is a 2D view of all A-scans from a specific set of elements corrected for delay and refracted angle (Figure 14).

Figure 13: Sectorial scanning used on turbine rotor.

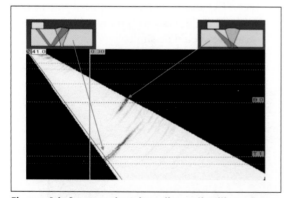

Figure 14: S-scan showing discontinuities at ID and OD.

Electronic Scans

Electronic scans are performed by multiplexing the same focal law (time delays) along an array (Figure 15). Typical arrays have up to 128 elements, but probes containing as many as 256 elements are not uncommon. Electronic scanning permits rapid coverage with a tight focal spot. If the array is flat and linear, then the scan pattern is a simple B-scan.

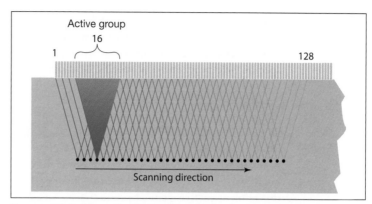

Figure 15: Schematic illustration of electronic scanning.

If the array is curved, then the scan pattern will be curved. Electronic scans are straightforward to program: for example, a phased array can be readily programmed to perform corrosion mapping, or to inspect a weld using 45° and 60° shear waves, which mimic conventional ASME manual inspections.

Combined Scans

Combining linear scanning, sectorial scanning, and precision focusing, for example, leads to a practical combination of displays (Figure 16). Optimal angles can be selected for welds and other components, while electronic scanning permits fast and functional inspections. For example, combining linear and L-wave sectorial scanning permits full ultrasonic inspection of components over a given angle range, such as +20°. This type of inspection is useful when simple normal beam inspections are inadequate, for example for titanium castings used in aerospace where discontinuiteies can have random orientations. A related approach applies to

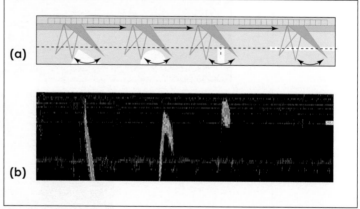

Figure 16: (a) Ultrasonic scanning pattern using sectorial and linear scanning; (b) ultrasonic image using data merged together.

weld inspections, where specific angles are often required for given weld geometries; for these applications, specific beam angles are programmed for specific weld bevel angles at specific locations.

Calibration

Some commonly used calibrations include sensitivity, variables and parameters, focusing effects, beam steering, and acquisition gates. Some infrequently used calibrations that are not addressed in this book are active element probe checks, wedge delay, velocity, exit point verification, and refraction angle verification.

Sensitivity

Sensitivity is important, and should be performed routinely. With S-scans, sensitivity is set using a block with defined side-drilled holes at varying depths, and compensated accordingly. Figure 17 shows a sample calibration procedure for a portable phased array unit.

Variables and Parameters

- Distance amplitude correction (DAC) is a method of compensating for attenuation, scatter, and other factors that reduce the signal amplitude as the beam penetrates the material. In practice, a DAC curve is drawn using a series of calibration reflectors at different depths to produce a series of different amplitudes at different depths.

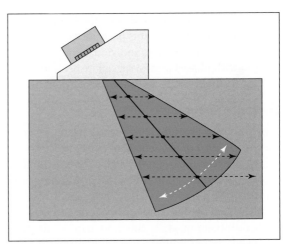

Figure 17: The array is rastered back and forth to obtain reflected signals from the calibration holes.

- Time corrected gain (TCG) and time variable gain (TVG) are similar to DAC, but the signal amplitudes are electronically compensated to all reach a predefined threshold (often 80%). Figure 18 shows sample calibration traces for three different S-scan angles.
- Angle corrected gain (ACG) compensates for the different amplitudes at different angles in an S-scan. These differences arise due to conversion efficiencies, which typically provide their strongest signals at the natural wedge angle. Once TCG and ACG have been performed, all the signal amplitudes within the calibrated S-scan pie should be similar.

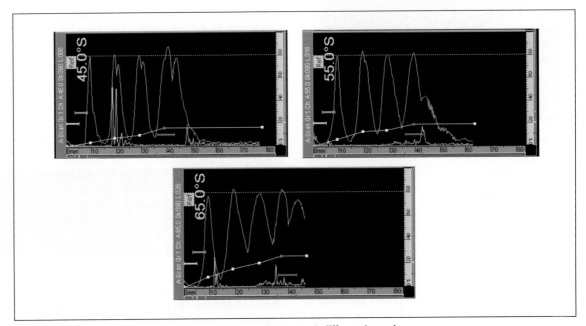

Figure 18: Sample calibration traces from an S-scan at different angles.

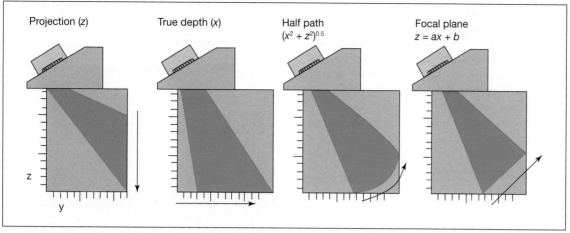

| Projection (z) | True depth (x) | Half path $(x^2 + z^2)^{0.5}$ | Focal plane $z = ax + b$ |

Figure 19: Typical focusing planes for phased arrays.

Focusing Effects

Focusing can only be performed within the near zone. In many cases with PA, the near zone occurs within the wedge, or not far into the metal, so focusing is effectively useless. Consequently, the current recommendation is not to focus for general scanning of welds, but to refocus if any specific discontinuities are detected for better imaging. Figure 19 shows possible focusing planes.

Beam Steering

Beam steering should only occur when the beam is within the natural arc of the individual elements. Note that operating outside the natural arc does not stop beam forming as such, but will significantly degrade the signals. The signal degrades because at higher angles, the grating lobe will take a higher proportion of the total sound pressure compared to the main lobe, thus the main lobe will require more amplification to detect a reflector and the base noise level will be higher.

Acquisition Gates

The acquisition gates for phased array instruments are similar to those for conventional ultrasonics. However, phased array instruments tend to be more expensive, so tend to have more gates. Automated inspection for tubular products or bar products typically use from 1 to 3 gates to better localize the discontinuities.

Data Collection
Encoded Scans

Two encoded scans commonly used are linear scans and raster scans. *Note:* Unless performed by manual raster scans without encoders, time-based data storage is not permitted under the ASME code due to variations in speed of travel and reproducibility.

Linear Scans
Linear scans are performed using encoded scanners and can store all the collected data. The data is then reprocessed and displayed as appropriate.

Raster Scans
Raster scans use a phased array unit as a conventional system, but an array to give multiple inspection angles. This offers some advantages due to higher scan speeds with multiple angles, and also to better imaging. However, raster scanning is significantly slower than encoded scanning.

Zone Discrimination

Zone discrimination is a unique inspection process for narrow gap welds where each beam is focused and directed at the appropriate angle to a specific facet of the weld. Thus spot-focused beams are driven around the weld at high speed to give 100% coverage of all areas, specifically for unusual weld profiles.

Scan Plans and Exam Coverage

As per code, both S-scans (sectorial) and E-scans (electronic) require scan plans to show coverage.

Typically, these scan plans can be provided by simple ray tracing programs, which show if coverage is sufficient and appropriate angles are used.

We can add the following information in the scan plan, or anywhere else judged appropriate: the number of virtual probe apertures (VPA) per probe, which depends on the total number of elements of the complete array ($\#Els_{array}$); the number of elements in a specific focal law ($\#Els_{VPA}$); and the element spacing between consecutive VPA (S), as detailed by Equation 4:

$$(Eq.\ 4)\qquad \#VPA = \frac{\left(\#Els_{array} - \#Els_{VPA}\right)}{S} + 1$$

When this value does not render a round unit, the decimal is rounded to the lowest unit. That means some elements are not used.

For example, one wants to use VPA of 16 elements and space these VPA by 5 elements to ensure proper coverage within 3 dB throughout the 128-element phased array probe. The total number of VPA will then be:

$$\#VPA = \frac{(128-16)}{5} + 1 = 23\ VPA$$

The real answer is 23.4. That means some elements are not used. In fact, the first 126 elements are used in this case and elements 127 and 128 are not.

Probe Offsets and Indexing

Probe offsets can be programmed into the phased array instrument to optimize inspections. A wedge delay can be applied to offset the sound path in acrylic, which is not relevant information for inspection or for A-scan signal interpretation. These offsets should come from the scan plan software.

Indexing is used to offset by a specific value each virtual probe aperture (VPA) from one another along the array. Indexing is performed for thicker materials. Encoded scans with indexing capability are required.

Procedures

Specific Applications

Material Evaluations
Phased arrays are used to evaluate a variety of materials. Examples of uses for material evaluation

include composites (Figure 20), nonmetallic materials, metallic materials, base materials, bar, rod, rail, forgings, and castings.

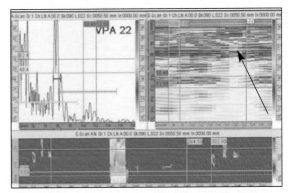

Figure 20: Example of phased array inspection of composites with discontinuities present.

Component Evaluations

Complex Geometries
Complex geometries can be a challenge, and typically require a suitable mock-up and/or calibration block before inspection. Components that may cause challenges because of their shapes include: turbines, shafts, keyways, nozzles, and flanges.

One of the major limitations of ultrasonics generally is the presence of geometric reflectors from complex shapes. These can be more readily identified with phased arrays, but may still require damping or other treatment to positively identify them.

Weld Inspections
When inspecting fabrication welds, inservice welds, or austenitic welds, it is important to know the materials and the types of discontinuities that are most common.

Fabrication or construction welds are defined by their potential deterministic discontinuities, such as fusion line discontinuities. Inservice inspections look for service-induced discontinuities such as cracks. Austenitic welds are difficult to inspect because of beam skewing, attenuation, or diffraction.

Data Presentations

With fully recorded data, encoded phased arrays can display almost any combination of data. Manual phased arrays, in contrast, typically only display A-scans and S-scans.

Once recorded, the encoded phased array data can be reprocessed to give a variety of other scans, for example D-scans, multiple displays, and S-scans. Many phased array systems can display multiple scans with additional TOFD and other data. Manual phased arrays do not generally offer these opportunities.

Data Evaluation

Codes, Standards, and Specifications

By and large, the main industry standard codes recognize phased array technology. The ASME code has numerous code cases and appendices covering phased array inspections, while ASTM has published Standard Practices for test setup and the performance of PA inspections. API accepts phased array testing, while AWS codes are still considering the acceptance of encoded arrays.

Discontinuity Characterization and Dimensioning

Discontinuity characterization is performed the same as with manual ultrasonics for manual PA; discontinuities are analyzed by manipulating the array to determine the number of dimensions, 2D or 3D. With encoded scans, such characterizations may not be possible.

Discontinuity dimensioning uses either amplitude-based approaches or diffraction approaches. The diffraction approach works well for height sizing with phased arrays, particularly in back diffraction, as the discontinuity tips are often detectable (Figure 21).

Reporting

Most phased array instruments have built-in reporting capabilities. These can be easily called up to supply a report, with almost all the information required by an operator. The selected images can be automatically pasted into this report.

Plotting is not complicated with phased arrays; a true depth S-scan or E-scan can be easily set up to show the locations of discontinuities in OD, ID, or midwall, for example, as in Figure 22.

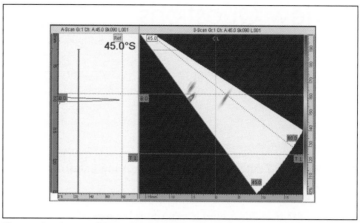

Figure 21: Back diffraction S-scan with crack tip visible.

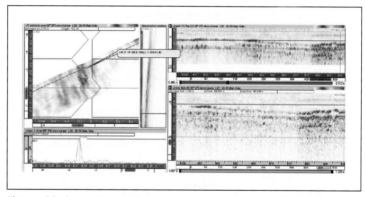

Figure 22: Sample overlay plot on E-scan (top left) with lack of sidewall fusion discontinuities visible.

Review Questions

1. Which is a difference between medical and industrial ultrasound?

   a. Medical ultrasound is hazardous because of radiation.
   b. Industrial ultrasound uses longitudinal and shear wave modes.
   c. Medical ultrasound uses shear waves.
   d. There are no differences.

2. What are industrial phased arrays used to inspect?

   a. Materials with similar properties.
   b. Bodies of humans and animals.
   c. Components with different geometries, materials, and discontinuities.
   d. Complex images based on diffraction patterns.

3. If there is no difference when switching from conventional ultrasonics to phased arrays, then:

   a. phased arrays should give essentially the same results as conventional UT.
   b. phased arrays should have much stronger signal amplitudes.
   c. phased arrays should have much weaker signal amplitudes.
   d. the diffraction patterns and grating lobes from phased arrays will interfere with the results.

4. What advantage does phased array have over conventional UT?

   a. Phased array is less expensive.
   b. Phased arrays are less complex because they have only one element.
   c. Phased arrays can be steered and focused.
   d. Phased arrays use less energy.

5. What condition must exist to focus a phased array?

   a. The focal point must be longer than the near field length.
   b. The focal point must be in the dead zone.
   c. The phased array must be high frequency.
   d. The focal point must be within the near zone.

6. What is an ultrasonic phased array?

   a. An array of ultrasonic elements electrically and acoustically connected.
   b. An array of ultrasonic elements pulsed simultaneously.
   c. An array of ultrasonic elements individually wired, pulsed, and time shifted.
   d. An array of ultrasonic elements coupled to the same A/D converter with an amplified background.

7. What is a benefit of ultrasonic phased array probes compared to conventional UT probes?

   a. Phased arrays can detect smaller discontinuities.
   b. Sound beams can be electronically steered, scanned, and focused.
   c. Phased arrays can use higher frequencies.
   d. Phased arrays are identical to conventional UT probes.

8. What could a UT inspector do to improve the probability of detection?

   a. Switch from a linear (1D) array to a matrix (2D) array.
   b. Switch from a larger array to a smaller array to get better contact and beam forming.
   c. Use electronic focusing to optimize the sound beam.
   d. Use a conventional single-element probe.

9. How is a sound beam formed with an ultrasonic phased array?

    a. Individual elements generate a beam that constructively and destructively interferes to form a wave front.
    b. The ferromagnetic field constricts the acoustic field and directs it into the part.
    c. Individual electrons are steered by deflection grids to create a coherent beam.
    d. The sound beam is created by pitch and elevation of the array.

10. What is a focal or delay law?

    a. The equation for determining the refracted angle of a sound beam.
    b. A natural law of physics governing the piezoelectric effect.
    c. A program to calculate the relative time delays between the various pulsing elements of a phased array.
    d. A calculation to determine effective scan width.

11. To switch from conventional UT to phased arrays, the operator should:

    a. review in depth the equivalent conventional UT inspection, and double the array size.
    b. study all drawings to determine any likely geometric reflectors.
    c. start by using the same aperture, frequency, focal length, and angle as for conventional UT.
    d. check the previous scans and evaluate any possible advantages.

12. What is the correct term for the center-to-center distance of phased array elements?

    a. Volume fraction.
    b. Pitch.
    c. Aperture.
    d. Virtual probe.

13. What is the passive aperture or elevation of an ultrasonic phased array?

    a. The sum of the element pitch and the gap.
    b. The difference between the length of the array and the number of elements.
    c. The length of all the individual elements of an ultrasonic array.
    d. The length of an individual array element.

14. What is a benefit of the active aperture plane of an ultrasonic phased array? The active aperture:

    a. is always constant.
    b. plane can be electronically focused.
    c. can be focused longer than the near field length.
    d. can be adjusted to display dispersion curves.

15. What is the difference between a 1D linear array and a 2D ultrasonic phased array?

    a. 2D arrays can be focused in both X and Y axes.
    b. 1D arrays are only good for angle beam inspections.
    c. 2D arrays can focus longer than the near field length.
    d. There are not any differences between 1D and 2D arrays.

16. How are ultrasonic phased arrays and conventional UT probes alike?

    a. Both use delay laws.
    b. Both use ferromagnetic principles.
    c. Both can only be focused within the near zone.
    d. Neither can be used for immersion testing.

17. What should an operator consider before choosing to do a manual or automated inspection?

    a. Determine if a scan plan is needed.
    b. Determine if higher scan speeds are appropriate for the test.
    c. Determine if the pulse repetition rate of the scanner will be exceeded.
    d. Determine if the test data needs to be archived.

18. When is zone discrimination used?

    a. When it is the fastest way to get the job done.
    b. When the ASME code permits the use of phased array.
    c. For narrow gap welds where each beam is focused and directed at the appropriate angle to a specific facet of the weld.
    d. Any time the operator wants to get more coverage.

19. Using the equation $\#VPA = (128 - A)/S + 1$, how many virtual probe apertures are in a 128-element linear probe using a 16-element aperture with a 5-element space?

    a. 16
    b. 23
    c. 64
    d. 128

Answers

1b	2c	3a	4c	5d	6c	7b	8c	9a	10c	11c	12b	13d
14b	15a	16c	17d	18c	19b							

CHAPTER 7
Codes and Standards

Ultrasonic examinations are usually performed in accordance with one or more procedures that are structured to comply with the rules and criteria of the applicable codes, specifications, standards and regulatory requirements (if applicable), and depending on the level of qualification of the inspector, written work instructions. The general hierarchy for these documents is as follows:

- Regulatory requirements (if applicable).
- Codes.
- Standards.
- Specifications.
- Inspection procedures.
- Written work instructions.

For a better understanding of what these documents cover, below is a brief general description of each type of document. It should be noted that some industries do not use codes, making standards the highest-level document. An example of this is the petroleum industry, whose top tier documents are American Petroleum Industry (API) standards.

Regulatory requirements are generally incorporated into the top tier document when the potential threat to the public safety is high. Examples of regulatory agencies are the U.S. Nuclear Regulatory Commission (USNRC) and the Federal Aviation Administration (FAA). USNRC has jurisdiction and regulatory control over all nuclear work involving radioactive materials and the FAA has a similar position in the aviation industry.

Codes are generally the governing documents, providing a set of rules that specify the minimum acceptable level of safety for manufactured, fabricated, or constructed objects. These may incorporate regulatory requirements and often refer to standards or specifications for specific details on how to perform the actual inspections (performance standards). Most codes will provide acceptance and rejection criteria for the required inspections, but often refer to the ASTM performance standards for the methodology used in applying the best nondestructive testing (NDT) method and technique.

Standards are documents that establish engineering or technical requirements for products, practices, methods, or operations. Of particular interest to NDT personnel are those standards that provide requirements for performing NDT tasks. An inspection standard may include information on how to apply multiple testing techniques, but usually does not include acceptance and rejection criteria, which are either specified by the governing code or the inspection purchaser's requirements.

Specifications provide specific additional requirements for materials, components, or services. They are often generated by private companies to address additional requirements applicable to a specific product or application. Specifications are often listed in procurement agreements or contract documents as additional requirements above and beyond code or standard requirements.

Inspection procedures are usually developed by the inspection company to provide details on how the inspection method or technique is to be applied (Table 1). These are generally based on the applicable performance standard but focus on one specific application, such as angle-beam UT, immersion UT, and phased array, for example. Ultrasonic procedures typically address the following items at a minimum:

- Instrument (selection, operating ranges).
- Calibration standard (tie-in to test materials).
- Search unit type, size, frequency (wave geometry).
- Screen settings (metal path).
- Area to be scanned (coverage intensity).
- Scanning technique (manual, coupling, automatic).
- Indications to be recorded (minimum sensitivity).
- Data record format (forms to be followed).
- Accept/reject criteria (basis or specification reference).
- Personnel qualifications (certifications).

The degree to which these and other items are controlled is usually dependent upon the criticality of the application.

Ultrasonic Testing Method | CHAPTER 7

Written work instructions provide step-by-step specific inspection instructions to be followed by Level I inspectors who cannot work on their own. These may be as explicit as describing the exact brand of inspection equipment; the length of coaxial cable to be used; the make, model, and specifications of the transducer; a specific gain setting; where to place the transducer; and so on.

The United States uses what is known as a free market system of standards development. Independent, nongovernmental organizations (standards bodies) develop codes and standards by using a consensus process and working with industry subject-matter experts. For a code or standard to be classified as an American National Standard (ANS), precise steps must be taken in the

development and maintenance processes, and those processes are reviewed and approved by the American National Standards Institute (ANSI), another independent organization. In many other countries this function is performed by various government agencies.

Code Bodies and Their UT Standards

There is an interesting relationship between codes and standards and their developers. Most NDT performance standards are developed by ASTM International (formerly the American Society for Testing and Materials). Most other U.S. codes and standards reference the applicable ASTM testing standards rather than duplicate that effort. They

Table 1: Typical code and standard requirements.

Issue	Approaches	Examples
Transducer selection	Ranges (size and angle) Prescribed angles Angles for each case	... transducers between 40° and 80° ... transducers of 45°, 60°, 70° ... 45° in mid-section, 70° near surface
Scan techniques	General coverage Intervals Overlap Scanning levels Rates	... use 9 in. centers for grid ... overlap each pass by 10% of active area ... scan sensitivity to be 6 dB above ref. ... maximum scan rate of 6 in. per sec.
Calibration	Instrument Transducers Distance correction Schedule	... vertical, horizontal linearity ... beam location (IIW), depth resolution, response from SDH, FBH, notch ... set DAC at 80% FSH, electronic settings ... recalibrate at start, shift, changes
Special problems	Component curvature Transfer	Use Figure XX to correct for curved items Use dual transducers to set transfer
Reporting	Formats/forms Analysis Authorizations	Form XYZ to be used in recording data Classification of reflector found by ... All reports signed by Level II & III
Acceptance criteria	General types Dimensions Collections	Reject all cracks and lack of fusion Reject slag over 3/4 in. in 2 in. plate Reject pore spacing of 3 within 2 in.
Personnel certification	Per undefined procedure Per SNT-TC-1A Per NAS-410 or NAVSEA 250-1500	Supplier to have certification program Written practice to SNT-TC-1A Procedure per ...
Records of examination	List of documentation Retention period	Final documentation shall include ... Supplier to retain records for 5 years

may incorporate additional requirements above and beyond the ASTM documents if it is felt those core documents do not sufficiently address the specific needs of the referencing code.

In the case of the *American Society of Mechanical Engineers* (ASME) *Boiler and Pressure Vessel Code*, many ASTM standards are incorporated into the code in their entirety. In the code, the ASTM E designation is changed to SE. For example, *ASTM E 164* becomes *SE 164* and the notation that the SE document is identical to the ASTM document is added.

Another difference between various codes and standards is how they address the details of the inspection process. For example, the AWS D1.1: *Structural Welding Code — Steel* has very specific requirements for wedge angle selection based on material thickness. It specifies strict transducer size and frequency, uses an International Institute of Welding (IIW) calibration, and uses an amplitude-based formula for determining a defect rating. That rating is then compared to a table that determines whether the indication is acceptable or not.

On the other hand, the ASME Code in Section V, Nondestructive Examination, provides specific instructions for calibrating a UT scope for weld inspections using a distance amplitude correction (DAC) curve and specifies a frequency range, but leaves the choice of transducer size and frequency within that range up to the inspector.

Below are some of the most commonly used U.S. code or standards bodies and some of the commonly used UT standards.

ASTM International

ASTM International is one of the largest voluntary standards development organizations in the world, providing technical standards for materials, products, systems, and services. Over 180 ASTM NDT standards are published in the *ASTM Annual Book of Standards, Volume 03.03, Nondestructive Testing*. Many of these standards provide guidance on how NDT test methods are applied, but they do not provide acceptance/rejection criteria. ASTM defines three of their document categories as follows:

- A **guide** is a compendium of information, or a series of options, that does not recommend a specific course of action. A guide increases the awareness of information and approaches in a given subject area.

- A **practice** is a definitive set of instructions for performing one or more specific operations or functions that does not produce a test result. Examples of practices include, but are not limited to: application, assessment, cleaning, collection, decontamination, inspection, installation, preparation, sampling, screening, and training.

- A **test method** is a definitive procedure that produces a test result. Examples of test methods include, but are not limited to: identification, measurement, and evaluation of one or more qualities, characteristics, or properties.

A partial list of some of the more commonly used ASTM UT standards follows. Additional standards can be found in the *ASTM Annual Book of Standards, Volume 03.03, Metals Test Methods and Analytical Procedures/Nondestructive Testing*.

- *ASTM E 114: Strandard Practice for Ultrasonic Pulse-Echo Straight-Beam Examination by the Contact Method*
- *ASTM E 164: Standard Practice for Contact Ultrasonic Testing of Weldments*
- *ASTM E 213: Standard Practice for Ultrasonic Testing of Metal Pipe and Tubing*
- *ASTM E 273: Standard Practice for Ultrasonic Testing of the Weld Zone of Welded Pipe and Tubing*
- *ASTM E 587: Standard Practice for Ultrasonic Angle-Beam Contact Testing*
- *ASTM E 797/E 797M: Standard Practice for Measuring Thickness by Manual Ultrasonic Pulse-Echo Contact Method*
- *ASTM E 1962: Standard Practice for Ultrasonic Surface Testing Using Electromagnetic Acoustic Transducer (EMAT) Techniques*
- *ASTM E 2373: Standard Practice for Use of the Ultrasonic Time of Flight Diffraction (TOFD) Technique*
- *ASTM E 2375: Standard Practice for Ultrasonic Testing of Wrought Products*
- *ASTM E 2580: Standard Practice for Ultrasonic Testing of Flat Panel Composites and Sandwich Core Materials Used in Aerospace Applications*
- *ASTM E 2700: Standard Practice for Contact Ultrasonic Testing of Welds Using Phased Arrays*

American Society of Mechanical Engineers (ASME)

ASME is a not-for-profit professional organization that enables collaboration, knowledge sharing, and skill development across all engineering disciplines, while promoting the vital role of the engineer in society. ASME codes and standards, publications, conferences, continuing education, and professional development programs provide a foundation for advancing technical knowledge and a safer world. ASME publishes multiple codes and standards including, but not limited to, the following documents.

The ASME *Boiler and Pressure Vessel Code* (BPV) is made up of 12 numbered sections, or "books," covering the following subjects:

I. Power Boilers
II. Materials
III. Rules for Construction of Nuclear Facility Components
IV. Heating Boilers
V. Nondestructive Examination
VI. Recommended Rules for the Care and Operation of Heating Boilers
VII. Recommended Guidelines for the Care of Power Boilers
VIII. Pressure Vessels
IX. Welding and Brazing Qualifications
X. Fiber-Reinforced Plastic Pressure Vessels
XI. Rules for In-service Inspection of Nuclear Power Plant Components
XII. Rules for Construction and Continued Service of Transport Tanks

The BPV is published biennially in odd-numbered years without addenda in the intervening year.

ASME B31.1, *Power Piping*. This code contains requirements for piping systems typically found in electric power-generating stations, industrial institutional plants, geothermal heating systems, and heating and cooling systems.

ASME B31.3, *Process Piping*. This code contains requirements for piping typically found in petroleum refineries; chemical, pharmaceutical, textile, paper, semiconductor, and cryogenic plants; and related processing-plant terminals.

American Welding Society (AWS)

The American Welding Society (AWS) is a nonprofit organization with the goal of advancing the science, technology, and application of welding and related joining disciplines. AWS provides certification programs for welding inspectors, supervisors,

and educators, and publishes multiple standards, many of which contain procedures for the application of nondestructive testing methods and techniques above and beyond visual inspection. A few of their standards are listed here:

- AWS D1.1: *Structural Welding Code – Steel*
- AWS D1.2: *Structural Welding Code – Aluminum*
- AWS D1.3: *Structural Welding Code – Sheet Steel*
- AWS D1.5: *Bridge Welding Code*
- AWS D1.6: *Structural Welding Code – Stainless Steel*

American Petroleum Institute (API)

The American Petroleum Institute (API) is a national trade association that represents all aspects of America's oil and natural gas industry, including producers, refiners, suppliers, pipeline operators, marine transporters, and service and supply companies. Among the standards that API publishes are the following:

- API 510: *Pressure Vessel Inspection Code: In-Service Inspection, Rating, Repair and Alteration*
- API 570: *Piping Inspection Code: In-Service Inspection, Rating, Repair, and Alteration of Piping Systems*
- API 650: *Welded Tanks for Oil Storage*
- API 653: *Tank Inspection, Repair, Alteration, and Reconstruction*
- API 1104: *Welding of Pipelines and Related Facilities*

Aerospace Industries Association (AIA)

The Aerospace Industries Association (AIA) is a trade association with more than 100 major aerospace and defense member companies. These companies embody every high-technology manufacturing segment of the U.S. aerospace and defense industry from commercial aviation and avionics, to manned and unmanned defense systems, to space technologies and satellite communications.

The AIA publishes multiple aviation and aerospace-related standards, two of which are:

- NAS 410, *NAS Certification and Qualification of Nondestructive Test Personnel*. This employer-based certification standard establishes the minimum requirements for the qualification and certification of personnel performing nondestructive testing (NDT), nondestructive inspection (NDI), or nondestructive evaluation

(NDE) in the aerospace manufacturing, service, maintenance, and overhaul industries. In 2002, NAS 410 was harmonized with European Norm 4179 (listed in the CEN section), so that the requirements in both documents are identical.

- NAS 999, *Nondestructive Inspection of Advanced Composite Structures*. This specification establishes the requirements for nondestructive inspection (NDI), NDI standards, NDI methods, and NDI acceptance criteria.

National Board of Boiler and Pressure Vessel Inspectors (NBBI)

The National Board of Boiler and Pressure Vessel Inspectors (NBBI) is a nonprofit organization that promotes greater safety to life and property through uniformity in the construction, installation, repair, maintenance, and inspection of pressure equipment. The National Board membership oversees adherence to laws, rules, and regulations relating to boilers and pressure vessels. NBBI provides training, and it issues inservice and new construction commissions for Authorized Inspectors (AIs), Authorized Nuclear Inspectors (ANIs), and Authorized Nuclear In-service Inspectors (ANIIs).

NBBI publishes the *National Boiler Inspection Code* (NBIC), which provides standards for the installation, inspection and repair, and/or alteration of boilers, pressure vessels, and pressure-relief devices.

Military Standards

For years the U.S. Department of Defense maintained its own military standards, usually using the designator MIL-STD-###. Many of these standards, because of their highly restricted applications to certain components and configurations, tended to establish more structured approaches to specific configurations of test parts and required inspection personnel to use these customized approaches when conducting ultrasonic inspections. However, in the interest of reducing costs and duplication of effort, over the past 10 to 15 years the DOD has been cancelling many military standards and specifying industry standards such as AMS, NAS, or ASTM specifications as the superseding documents. For example, MIL-STD-2154 has been replaced by AMS-STD-2154 and MIL-STD-1949 has been replaced by *ASTM E 1444*.

Review Questions

1. Additional company requirements would most likely be found in which of the following documents?

    a. A code.
    b. A standard.
    c. A specification.
    d. An inspection procedure.

2. Which type of document would contain specific information on equipment selection and scanning area?

    a. A code.
    b. A standard.
    c. A specification.
    d. An inspection procedure.

3. Which of the following personnel are required to work to specific written instructions?

    a. Trainees.
    b. Level I.
    c. Level II.
    d. Both Level I and Level II.

4. Which of the following organizations writes the majority of NDT performance standards?

    a. ASTM.
    b. ASME.
    c. AWS.
    d. ANSI.

5. Inspection procedures are usually based on which of the following documents?

    a. A work instruction.
    b. A standard.
    c. A specification.
    d. A regulatory requirement.

6. What system of development is used in the United States to develop standards?

    a. Free market.
    b. Government oversight.
    c. For-profit industry.
    d. Regulatory agencies.

7. Which of the following organizations is responsible for issuing commissions to Authorized Inspectors, Authorized Nuclear Inspectors, and Authorized Nuclear In-service Inspectors?

    a. ASTM International.
    b. The American Society of Mechanical Engineers.
    c. The National Board of Boiler and Pressure Vessel Inspectors.
    d. The American National Standards Institute.

8. Which document would a person use to learn about the requirements for a pressurized heat exchanger?

    a. AWS D1.2: *Welding Code.*
    b. API 650.
    c. *ASTM E 2375.*
    d. ASME BPV, Section VIII.

Answers

1c	2d	3b	4a	5b	6a	7c	8d

FIGURE SOURCES

All figures are derived from sources published by The American Society for Nondestructive Testing, Inc., except for the following used with permission:

Chapter 2

Figure 1 - Jim Houf.

Chapter 3

Figures 3, 4, 9, 10 - Jim Houf.

Chapter 4

Figures 5, 6 - Jim Houf.

Chapter 5

Figures 1, 10, 12, 14, 16, 17, 19, 20, 21, 22 - courtesy of Olympus.

Figures 2–9, 11, 13, 15, 18, 23–29, 31-37 - Dave Mandina.

Figure 30 - courtesy of ES Beam Tool.

Chapter 6

Figures 1–11, 13–22 - courtesy of Olympus.

Figure 12 - courtesy of EPRI.